# Hidden Depths

## The life and loves of a young gravedigger.

**Peter Street**

**PreeTa** ✴ **Press**

## Foreword

'I have done so many jobs ranging from Forester, Head Gardener, Chef, Taxi Driver, Writer in Residence in prisons, schools, International Youth Camps, B.B.C Greater Manchester Radio, poet in the Croatian/Bosnian conflict, to name but a few. Yet being a Gravedigger/Exhumer in Bolton when I was eighteen was one of the jobs I enjoyed most.

'Maybe because of my lack of education or my various disabilities I don't really know, but whatever it was, the graveyards and those seven gravediggers seemed to set me up for whatever life was going to throw at me.'

Peter Street

**Warning!**

*Please be advised that this book is not for the faint hearted. Amongst other things it contains details of corpses, burials and re-internments.*

## Dedication

**"to Sandra for her patience."**

## Acknowledgements

Rite of Passage, an earlier version of this book, was edited by Mick Bruce & issued as an ebook by Natterjack Press in 2013.

This book has been revised & re-edited by Preeta Press and contains substantial new material and notes as well as a new name.

Front cover photograph by Peter Street

Back cover photograph by John Bentley

Design by Preeta Press 2018

Hidden Depths – Peter Street

Published in 2018 by

Preeta Press, Bolton, Greater Manchester

preetapress.com

All Rights Reserved

Copyright Peter Street, 2018

ISBN:  978-1-9998489-2-7

Printed by Printdomain Ltd,

## By the same Author

**Listen To The Dark** – *Penniless Press (2012)*

**Not Cawed Firewood Fa Now't** – *ShoeString Press (2010)*

**Thumbing from Lipik to Pakrac** – *Waterloo Press (2008)*

**Tony Bevan and Peter Street at The Turnpike Gallery, Leigh** *(2006)*

**Trees will be Trees ShoeString** - *Press (2001)*

**Still Standing** – *Towpath Press (1997)*

**Out Of The Fire** – *Spike Books (1993)*

Peter is a recipient of a Royal Literary Fund Grant and a
member of the Society of Authors

## Contents

Hidden Depths – Peter Street

## Chapter 1

### Sand

*November 1967. Astley Bridge Cemetery.*
In the gravediggers' cabin there were three cemetery workers sitting at the table. All three were pulling hard on Woodbines. The biggest of the three came over, introduced himself as Arnold.

His hand completely enclosed mine, his bottom two knuckles were out of line, his wrist bone seemed big. I'd seen this before with the fairground workers known as the Gaff lads or Gaffs. He'd been a bare-knuckle fighter.
Rick, the youngest of the three, with tattoos and a Brian Jones' hairstyle, nodded at me from across the table. He leaned forward and took the fag from the guy opposite who had fallen asleep in mid-sentence whilst talking to Rick. The sleeping guy suddenly jerked awake, but then, shortly afterwards, fell back to sleep with another lit fag in his hand.

One week later, I was given my first ever four-foot-six-inch grave. Rick helped me build the wooden staging at a forty-degree slant, so the earth would be easier to fill back in later. He reassured me about it being easy on the Church of England patch. Easy, until we hit water, three-foot later. Rick, to stop me from sinking, brought me a slate to stand on. Fine, until a rising stench of the bodies below hit me, a mixture of sulphur and diarrhoea. It was now a dig in a stinking black porridge. After pulling on a Woodbine, Rick climbed down the wooden sides to show me how to slant the grave floor and then dig a sump (a round hole lower than the floor) so the water would drain down into the hole and we could bucket it out from there. Easy, aye, once you know how!

After lunch, he brought three slates to lay over the coffin lid to protect our latest member from the backfill crashing through. Also, to safeguard the next digger from dropping in unannounced.

My first ever funeral and everything went perfect. On top, the undertaker gave me a five shillings tip. Rick smiled. Nodded, gave me the thumbs up. We became close friends. He taught me about keeping safe with wooden sides and head and foot blocks to hold open the graves, especially the very deep ones.

A month later it was my turn for a nine-footer; again, down on the Church of England section, in the part where he thought there was a good chance of hitting sand. Sand? I thought of Blackpool, sunbathing, donkeys, Punch and Judy. But Rick said for safety we needed to knock in more wooden sides to stop a sand flood and the stone kerbs from dropping in. Our wooden sides were almost touching each other.
Seven feet down and having a rest when:
   "Running sand!" Rick shouted. He also yelled across the cemetery for Arnold, who was working nearby.
   "Running sand..."
 He leaned down to grab my hand. The sand was seeping behind and between our wooden sides down, down to the bottom of the grave where it was beginning to fill up. The wooden sides were starting to creak. I jumped up to grab his hand. Missed it. I tried again. Missed. The sand was gaining,

dropping faster than ever, the floor was rising up. Sand was now covering my clogs. I was being pulled down. I held my hands up for Rick to grab me. He wasn't there. Sand was now up to my ankles.

"Rick!"

The sides were beginning to loosen, slide, creak. I looked up again, sand was pulling my legs further down when Rick slid a nine-foot plank downwards and somehow wedged it solid. He tested it by sliding down on it, while holding on to what sides were still holding up. Neither of us spoke. The creaking was giving us louder and louder warnings. Yes, it was going to happen. Calm as best as I could be. Rick grabbed my hand and started pulling me up while trying to climb up the plank. It wasn't working. I stayed calmish!

He stayed in the grave with me and while we were waiting he offered me a Woodbine. We had no lighter - no matches.

The creaking and the speeding sand seemed to have stabilised.

"Have you ever had one of those days?" he asked.

I tried to smile but couldn't. Two minutes later, Arnold was looking down at us both from above, tutting the way he did. He undid his leather belt and keeping hold of one end, threw the other end down for Rick to grab hold of. I grabbed Rick's wrist and together with the help of the plank, Arnold, with those arms and huge hands, you could strop a razor on, muscled both of us up and out of the sand.

"Next time you're going to get yourself in the shit," Rick said, "can you make sure you have a light?"

I couldn't say anything. I had felt both fright and an excitement I had never experienced before! I knew I couldn't tell Mum. My God, she would've freaked out and my grave-digging days would have been over before they had really begun. The three of us were walking up to the cabin when Arnold took me to one side and out of the blue asked:

"Do you get a warning with your epilepsy?"
I nodded.

"As long as we know."

That was it. My epilepsy was never mentioned again.

The following day, there was a kiddie's bucket and spade waiting for me on the bench next to my clogs. I had passed my initiation. It was the first time I had ever been really tested. In a way it was also a test for them, which they also passed with flying colours. I was now one of them, a bona fide gravedigger. For the first time in my life, I felt I was someone.

### *A Kind of Village*
I was also now beginning to see the cemetery as a kind of village with all the normal occupants: police officers, post-workers, pensioners, children, nurses, doctors, soldiers, every type of person with a few cats and dogs thrown in for good measure.

\*\*\*

## Chapter 2

### Hands

*Winter 1967.*

My first ten-foot-six grave. The wet and cold was splitting open my hands. A cold yet burning heat. A burn I needed to cool and protect my hands from. Gloves were useless. The spade was still burning holes in the palms of my hands. I needed to dip them in ice. I was blowing on them to try and somehow take away the pain. Arnold came over to see how I was getting on and gruffly advised:

"You need to piss on your hands. That will ease the pain and help to heal them back to something like."

I just didn't believe piss would help/heal/ease the pain! 'Wash your hands after the toilet' was plastered on all the school walls and now I was being told to piss on my hands.

"They're your hands......please yourself."

Arnold turned, walked away while reminding me about the benefits of my own urine. He was mumbling something about pee and other cultures as he went, but I ignored his advice. I dug until five-feet down the stench hit me and my clothes began to stink of dead, rotting bodies. The burn in my hands was still there. I took a break, walked over to the church intending to put my hands under the cold-water tap as the freezing burn was worse than ever.

"Hello, Peter?" said a stranger who reminded me of my dad's friend Peter, who I had always called Uncle. The stranger wore his whiskers in the same style as Uncle Peter. His clothes were almost the same - as if it was a street uniform. The same length, same trench coat, same boots, same missing laces, almost the same pin badges filling the ex-army lapels.

"Yes, I can see you're Tommy's lad alright." There was no looking me up and down. No judging me.

"How is your dad?"

I didn't reply but looked at him warily.

"You're good for a pot of tea, then?" he asked.

"Who said that?" I asked defensively.

"Word gets around."

I was trying to think of something to say when he interrupted my thoughts:

"Why have you let your hands get in that state?"

He also talked about the benefits of pissing on your hands and not washing it off.

I shook my head.

He tutted.

I was going to push my hands under the cold water tap when he grabbed my wrist. His grip was strong, determined.

I glared at him.

My feelings were mixed. He could have been anyone, yet there was something about him. He let go of my hands and took a step back. His voice changed, calmly he said,

"Look, trust me, if you dip your hands under that cold water tap you could end up in hospital."

I was in the between worlds of mum, teachers, health professionals and such like and the pain of my hands. When he faced me, his words seemed to blow away some of my past learning. I went into the nearby toilet and pissed on my hands. The warm steam died in a few seconds. Maybe it was psychological but there seemed to be an instant easing of the pain.

"Now, how about a cup of tea?" He asked, "And could you save and leave your old newspapers in a corner over there in the church doorway for winter, please?"

He stressed, 'Please.'

I didn't reply.

From his jacket pocket he took out a tiny piece of coal and started sucking it.

"That's it. See you in a couple of months. Newspapers, please."

Thinking about it later, his accent wasn't northern. It wasn't working class. In fact, he didn't have an accent at all. Before leaving, he sparkle-cleaned his hands, ingrained with oil and dirt, using a tiny rub of soap and a spoonful of sugar. I'd never seen anyone wash in sugar before. I was about to make him tea but he'd taken off.

Gone.

Arnold was on the Catholic section spading out a nine-footer for a young Polish lad of sixteen, who, while playing tennis in Astley Bridge Park, had suddenly dropped dead. His young heart just stopped working. One week later he became the latest member of the Village, 'Our Village.'


After the funeral his mother came back when everyone had left. She was on her knees next to his grave. I wanted to put my arm around her and tell her, 'he's alright, the other Village kids will welcome him with open arms.' But how could I say something like that to her? She was going through enough trauma without

7

hearing something so off the wall - I could have been arrested for it.

Ten yards down from where the young Polish lad had settled in, was the O'Hara grave. I was about thirteen when O'Hara entered the Village. I remembered all those times when I used to hang out with his younger brother Michael, and that night when we were at the fairground and the Gaff lads grabbed him. I ran all the way back to his house quicker than I had ever run before.

That was the first time I saw O'Hara and his belt, and the way he took the belt out of a dark cupboard drawer and fixed it around his waist, all the while making sure he didn't cut himself on the razor blades sewn in between the sharpened silver studs. He strapped it around his waist, then settled it in place like a gunfighter. He always double-checked the quick release buckle, dropping it into his hand, then settling it back into its final resting place.

A few days later, shouts of 'Fight, Fight' resounded from the other side of Halliwell Road and it was rumoured to be taking place near Tipping's Brew, across the concrete road that bridged the stream.

This was where I often walked my dog Rex - my excuse for entering the grass wasteland we called the 'Cornfields.' The place where three giant clinkers sat, almost the size of buses, forming a perfect triangle. We all imagined they'd been dropped from outer space. Later, I found out they were lumps of 'Bessemer'.

Me and Rex from this side of the stream could just see into the triangle of giant clinkers, O'Hara and his gang were slashing the air with their studded belts. 'Fight, Fight' was still in the air, though the word was the battle between O'Hara's gang and the Teds, with their yellow drapes and purple creepers, would take place after tea.

That evening, Dad, top coat on, teeth in, took me down to Maxie's to buy me a Hop-along Cassidy wrist watch, followed by a treat of Nettle beer at Jack Sheff's Temperance Bar. There I heard that some Ted, with a flick knife, had cheated, not waiting for 'Go' or for the slashing of a studded belt, but had walked up and coolly stabbed O'Hara to death.

\*\*\*

## Chapter 3

### Stillborn

*Late Winter 1967.*

Ice cold water and mud were still ripping open my hands and the pain seemed worse than ever. Not only that, but it was my turn for a Stillborn. It felt so strange setting out only half of our usual staging. Old people, yes. Murderers and such like, of course. But babies, no! That's not part of the game. It just didn't seem natural.

There was a down mood all morning. Arnold asked if I wanted him to dig it. I was going to say yes, but then Rick came into the conversation saying I would have to face it sometime so why not now? We all knew he was right.

The three of us puffed on Woodbines. There were no jokes and none of Rick's fancy tricks with his Zippo lighter. Nothing but a loud silence. A few minutes later we broke the silence; first with the talk about how it was different from an adult funeral, how we normally take the coffin from the mourners, place it gently onto the staging, ropes through the rings, down they go. Easy! Stillborns, no! We have to be more professional than usual because we are the guys who have to take a tiny coffin from a heartbroken mother's arms. Trust. That's what it's all about.

There was something different about the two hardest men who I had ever met, who were now standing with me. Their talk was gentler. Rick asked me if I was alright. They asked about Sandra. They talked football. We shared cigarettes.

10

It was Arnold who spoke first:

"Try not to touch the mother's hands, but just in case, make sure your hands are as clean as they can possibly be."
He then started saying how before the cortège came in he wanted me in clean overalls.

Stage set, I was digging in half the usual length of a grave. My hands were still stinging, but that was OK as I wasn't on a ten-foot-six dig, though I still pissed on my hands. Rick laughed and shook his head, but I just got on with it. My hands were now half way to turning into sandpaper.

Eighteen inches down I hit water and, kneeling on a two-foot slate, I started to stab out the coffin shape in a solid tunnel of clay, where the Stillborn was going to rest under the white headstone of: 'Dear Beloved Grandfather...'

There was something strange about kneeling down in a grave. Even stranger was tunnelling while crunched up in such a small space. Yes, my breathing was laboured. I was out of breath. My chest was tight like I'd been running up a mountain. Rick grabbed and pulled me out, then jumped down saying it was his turn in the half grave. Rick was now down on his knees, stabbing the sides, his head disappearing into the dark three-foot long tunnel. He was talking while digging, how? He lit a fag and talked about how people chose different sizes and styles of coffins for their stillborn babies even though they were all probably around the same size. Then it was my turn to be back on the slate, looking down the 'black of forever'

11

and I could see how that extra foot or so Rick had cut out had made all the difference.

A couple of hours later the funeral party began to arrive, black beetle funeral cars were creeping in between angels standing either side of the green cast iron gates. They were passing the giant Romany stones. I never usually took much notice of most funeral cars coming in as I was always too busy making sure the green drapes were hiding the soil/clay. The soil/sandbox was sorted so it would be easy to grab a handful for dropping onto the tiny coffin. Everything was as it should be. The dig had been our hardest for all sorts of reasons, but it was ready.

The young woman carrying the tiny stillborn looked familiar. It was Jennifer, an old girl-friend. We had gone out for a couple of weeks, a kids' thing. Nothing serious, a first kiss, the odd squeeze. I hadn't seen her for years.

Shaking, she paused. The Undertaker went to help her. She refused and then forced her arms out towards me. Taking the two- foot long coffin from her I tried, really tried, not to look her in the face, but a quick glance got the better of me.
I stalled for a second or two before resting that tiny coffin onto the wooden staging. Tears were washing away her colour. I was determined to keep myself in control. I wanted to say something, but what? What could I say? Jennifer, the mother, was a lifetime older than her twenty years. 'What ifs' flooded my head. There was a look on her face, I thought it said, 'hello.' OK, it was probably me making too much of the look she gave me.

12

I climbed down into the grave. I was standing on granddad, the coffin below, the Undertaker handed me the tiny coffin. I then gently laid that tiny coffin down in the middle of the grave somewhere between grand-daddy's shoulders. I climbed out as best and as dignified as I could, and then disappeared behind some headstones out of view where I could keep myself together, whilst watching Jennifer.

Ten minutes later and it was all over, and I formally welcomed Baby into the Village and into the arms of his/her granddad. The Undertaker gave me a five shillings tip. I jumped down, placed a slate on the front side of the coffin to stop Baby from sliding out.
Then out and on with the job of backfilling faster than I had ever done. After moving away from the staging, I ripped open the backs of the sprays/bouquets to give them air to breathe and a chance to live longer.
I brushed and picked up any clay crumbs from the dig and placed them onto the small mound. About 4pm: half an hour to go before the end of the shift, a car pulled in, stopping front side of the church. Jennifer, still in her mourning clothes, stepped out. She was walking towards her baby's grave when I had an overwhelming urge to run down to her. She was down on her knees sobbing. But I couldn't do or say anything that might help her. I stayed out of sight while her mother held her then took her back to the waiting car.

It was my turn to stay behind, making sure the church was locked up and secured on the coldest day of that year. It was

13

almost dark, I was searching my overall pockets for the church keys when I heard a familiar voice.

There was no-one there.

I looked around, no-one.

I walked around to the back of the church: no-one.

I looked across the cemetery. Nothing, except the usual gravestones popping up, while saying goodnight to everyone. Nothing else.

There was a humming, 'Que Sera, Sera.' but there was no-one there. Again, humming. No-one. I pushed open the church door and the friend of Uncle Peter, his trousers around his ankles, was lagging his legs with those saved newspapers. Casually he said:

"Hello."

"What? I mean. Why? I mean…what are you doing?"

"I'm doing what I'm doing."

There was no answer to that.

The windows were frosted. I didn't have the heart to order him to leave.

"Stay in here if you want to."

He started pushing newspapers into his palliasse. Satisfied, he lay on top of it and covered himself with the other newspapers and said, "Thanks."

The hut would have been better, warmer, except that the Foreman had a problem with us being amiable with the 'road' men. This was the reason he checked the hut before any of us arrived every morning.

Next day it was freezing but dry in the church doorway. Because it had been so cold, I was expecting a body, but he had

14

gone. The newspapers had been stacked where they had been before. It looked like no one had been there at all.

\*\*\*

## Chapter 4

### Sandra

That weekend me and Sandra walked into the Co-op jewellers facing Bolton Town Hall and asked if we could see some engagement rings. She picked a diamond ring set in platinum.

"Do you need credit?"

"No, thanks."

I ripped twenty-one pound notes from a roll of twenty-eight and then slapped it (not too hard) on the counter.

But, we were having problems with our parents, Mum was wrapping me in her cotton wool again and Sandra never found out who had grassed us up to her Mum and Dad about us kissing on the bench in Queens Park. She was banned from seeing me. How could a gravedigger provide for a family? That was one of their arguments. Sandra went hysterical.

Later, Mum was saying something about Sandra not being right for me. All of Bolton must have heard when I shouted:

"I'm going to marry Sandra!"

With that, I picked up my work clobber and crammed it into a duffel bag together with some clean clothes, not forgetting my important tablets and medication, then walked out. I had the keys to the cemetery and the gravediggers' cabin. So I spent a night in the cabin on the bench above the stinking clogs. Fortunately, more by luck than judgement, it had been my turn to lock and unlock everything. But it was for one night only.

Next morning, the Foreman said I had to move out, but later handed me a newspaper with some flats/bedsits/rooms in Eckersley Road, about a mile from the cemetery, circled in pencil. I decided to look at one of the underlined ones. Eckersley Road was only a hundred yards or so from my old home on Blackburn Road, but I didn't think about that, I was desperate.

A big hard looking woman opened the door, almost as though she had been lying in wait, it was that quick. I was so nervous when I asked,

"I'm looking for a room, I was told there might be one here?"

"Oh, you did, did you?" She answered with a strong Irish accent.

She folded her arms across her ample chest, looked me up and down and asked:

"How old are you?"

"Eighteen."

"More like sixteen!"

I showed her the advert.

"Yes, that's mine, OK."

Her questioning and the looks she gave me couldn't have been more intense. The way she asked questions was almost threatening. She was insistent on me telling her about what I did and where I worked.

"I'm a gravedigger."

"So, you're on the spade then?"

I nodded.

"Only donkeys nod," she said.

It felt like I was somehow being tested.

"I'm a gravedigger," I said again, proudly.

"Jesus, Mary and Joseph."
Surreal didn't even come close, especially when she asked
which church I went to. I was thinking, 'why would she want to
know that?' All I wanted was a place to stay for a few days
until I got things sorted. That was it. Nothing more. Her arms
were right across her chest. Her jaw was pulled up tight as if
she was expecting a punch.

"St. Patrick's, on Great Moore Street."
 She stepped into my personal space. She knew she'd caught
me off guard.

"So, you're on the spade and you go to St. Patrick's?"
She gave way and pushed open the door. The long hallway was
weird. Really strange. It had been painted white, with red,
fancy lace curtains hanging down from the ceiling, yet there
were no windows. The carpet was green with specks of gold.
She closed the door behind me. There was a strong smell of
perfume about the place and it was deathly quiet.

Unexpectedly, she grabbed my shoulder and told me that I
must never go further down the corridor as it was no place for a
young man like myself. She then grabbed my arm, pulled me
into the first room on the left. She made it clear that I had to
stay in my room. She fiddled with a bunch of keys, making me
think she was going to change her mind. Then she slotted a key
into the door.

"It will be ten shillings a week."
I searched my pockets. 7/6d was all I had. She looked me up
and down, twiddled her crucifix.

"Owe it me."

## Hidden Depths – Peter Street

She switched on the light and told me about the gas meter which was fed with shillings. But I hadn't a penny more on me, so she walked over and slotted in a shilling and slapped another one on top of the gas meter box. She then walked further into the tiny room and flicked off a dust sheet from an easy chair sitting near the fireplace.

The paper on the wall over the bed was old and peeling off. There was a two-ring gas cooker facing a single bed with no blankets or sheets or anything to cover myself with. She again stepped into my space, reminding me sternly about the hallway. I knew from her sideways look she meant every word. I promised, even crossed my heart and hoped to die!

Alone, I pulled the bright red-lined curtains down from the huge double windows and used those heavy drapes for my blankets. Only then did I realise what I had done, and it frightened me.

Within five minutes of the landlady leaving me alone in that tiny room, there was a knock on the front door. Again, she was there within seconds, as though she was expecting someone. I couldn't fully hear what the man at the door was saying. But he was soon walking down the hallway where I didn't dare to tread.

Before long, there was another knock and less than five minutes after the first man, the second stranger was welcomed in to tread down that hallway. I peeked opened my door, a big man in his Sunday best was making his way down the hallway. He turned as though he knew I was there, though I think I managed to close the door quickly before he saw me.

"You know the way," I heard the land-lady say to him.

"I do," answered the big man with a strong Southern Irish accent.

There were two or three more knocks that night and each of the men, all Irish, were all wearing their Sunday best, as if they were going to Mass. Within an hour of each of them visiting, the men (more or less in the order they had entered) walked back up the hallway to the front door. I heard the landlady thank them while saying her goodbyes to each of them in turn.

\*\*\*

Nothing was said at the cemetery. I think they all knew. Why else would they bring in extra sandwiches to share with me? Rick had even brought in a meat pie that he said he couldn't eat and asked me if I would like it. I tried not to snatch it from his dirt-ingrained fingers.

That night I met Sandra in Bolton as pre-arranged. She had mixed feelings about me leaving home and how it would be more expensive to rent a room. She did understand the reasons, but was doubtful about it, especially when I told her about sleeping on a cold, dirty mattress in my clothes with just curtains for blankets. Then there was the number of men who visited the place. She wanted to see this place, especially as I had managed to get it for only 7/6 a week. The place where a very accommodating Irish woman was constantly at the door waiting for male visitors.

Sandra was not impressed at all. We first went back to her house and, without her parents knowing, she smuggled out her spare candlewick bedspread and some tins of tomato soup.

We later bought a box of candles. She took me for a meal at the Wimpy Bar and then treated me to one of their truly magnificent lemon meringue pies. Later, we walked the two miles or so up Blackburn Road to my bed-sit. Once there, I made her a cup of tea. Forgetting I had no milk or sugar. We sat on the bed, leaned against the wall and talked marriage plans and dreams. Sandra lit a candle, we lay holding on to each other: tight. Like nothing or no-one would be able pull us apart. The two of us were one.

\*\*\*

Another day and another grave to dig. I was given the next job. Six-foot-six, Church of England, which turned out to be an easy dig with no complications.
On the day of the funeral everything was ready. No idea who I was burying, though I knew it was a young guy in his late teens, the surname meant nothing to me or so I thought.

Two motorbikes led the procession into the Bridge followed by the hearse and other cars.

As the mourners gathered by the graveside, I realised I knew many of them. They were my friend Jack's family and some of my biker friends, but Jack wasn't there.

I'd met Jack just after I'd left school. I'd been bullied at school and decided I needed to muscle up and get better at handling myself. I went to the wrestling club on Silverwell Street and that's where I met him. He was a bit of an outsider too and we immediately clicked and became good friends. Later, when we both hung about with bikers (though neither of us had a bike) he became my best friend. He introduced me to the group I always thought of as the 'Razor Gang', with the words, "don't mess with them and they won't mess with you," I took him at his word and, fair enough, they never did.

Since going out with Sandra I'd lost touch with him (she never took to him) but now it looked like it was his funeral and I felt a bit guilty about losing our friendship. Some of his biker friends who I recognised, shouldered the coffin. After the body had been committed and the funeral was over, Jack's father came across and patted me on the back. That's when I was sure that it was Jack we'd just welcomed, and I was in shock and mourning as I picked up my spade to replace the earth.

I somehow couldn't leave the graveside as a great wave of sadness overcame me. I thought of the quiet lad who had accepted me and consoled me when I told him about being called 'slow' when I worked part time at the Cash & Carry warehouse. In many ways he was a mystery. He never talked about other friends or girlfriends, didn't comment like other boys about football or other sports. Yet I sensed a brilliance in him. He always dressed in a suit, unfortunately it was a bit grubby and his shirts had frayed collars, though his ties were OK and his shoes were always highly polished. An odd thing he used to do, which I've never heard of before or since, was to use Vaseline (instead of Brylcreem) to do his hair. He would take a blob from the round tin put it in his palm, warm it next to the fire until it became runny, then work it into his hair and

22

use a comb to make a quiff at the front and a perfect DA at the back. As the Vaseline cooled it would set his hair style solid for the whole day.

On the few times I was a bit depressed and untalkative, Jack would cheer me up by singing 'Goodbye', the song we'd heard Joseph Locke singing at the Whitehorse Inn. Once he started singing, I'd join in and we'd start marching away.

My last memory of Jack was walking with him through Queens Park. It started raining and within seconds our grey pants were dotted black by the rain drops, "Spotty Muldoon!" he quipped. Much later, I talked to a mutual friend who told me Jack had, had a chest infection, which we both assumed was pneumonia, and had been found dead in his bed holding a hot water bottle to his chest.

It's funny that people remember these odd facts when someone dies, though, I suppose in the case of a seemingly fit, young man, it's hard for everyone to come to terms with such a sudden, unexpected death.

I've buried a couple of school friends, but no funeral had such an impact on me as Jack's. I felt that no-one should die alone. Least of all Jack and with a hot water bottle on his chest. But that was him. Always alone and gone to his forever.

For years later, members of the 'Razor Gang' would stop me in town to talk about this and that and each time we'd remember Jack.

***

After a hard day's work, it was 5pm when I unlocked the door into my one room, shit hole, ready to collapse. After the shock and emotion of burying my once best friend, I didn't want to have to deal with anything else.

As I opened the door I was shocked to see Mum sitting on the bed. She held herself erect, like she always did when she meant business.

Relief walked me in. I wanted to hug and kiss her: I had missed her so much. I had missed everything a boy misses about his mother. Alright, her over protective 'Mum thing', at times really did get to me, but it was just her way of showing her love for me.

I was going to try and show her that I was doing OK, strong, proficient, independent when the door opened and in stepped the owner. Her arms folded over her huge bosom.

" See Kitty, he's not done so bad. I kept him well away from down there," she said while pointing to the hallway.
My mother didn't respond.
"How's Tommy?" the woman asked.
I was surprised that she knew my dad, he'd always warned me against Irish women and had always seemed to hate them
"He's being bothered with his eyes," my mother replied.
Then they started talking about 'women's things' - right there in front of me.
Finally, the landlady asked me,
"Are you going home, now?"
She stressed the 'Now'.

24

She pointed to my bag which had been packed.

"I think," the woman said, looking at my mum, "I've put everything in, at least everything I could find."

Mum thanked her.

The woman sort of smiled, asking:

"Are you going to St, Patrick's, again this Sunday? I'll be at the ten o'clock mass."

Mum nodded, smiled, and they hugged.


Outside, mum started to tell me how much dad had missed me. How he had cried after I had left and promised nothing like that would happen again and that Sandra would be welcomed by them both as part of the family.

And, later everything was as they had promised, they did welcome Sandra with open arms.

\*\*\*

A couple of days later, the foreman came into the diggers cabin, handing me a chit: six foot-six. New grave. Catholic section: 'Bretherton.' I didn't think twice about the name... It was a clean, dry dig. No problems. No stench. The staging was about a forty-degree angle, making the back-fill easier. A couple of hours or so later, the funeral party left the street outside behind them and carefully, nervously, anticipatory almost, crept in through the green cast iron gates.

There was something about the lady behind the bearers. I had a second look. Yes, it was! Miss Bretherton, my old school's music teacher; the tall blonde, Lana Turner look-a-like. Once, while crossing her legs, she accidentally flashed: just one blink, the top of her American Tan nylons together with the thinnest line of skin, white, secretive; except... well to me.

She was walking down the crunchy path, head up, proud like she was leading someone to meet the Queen. It seemed obvious to me that the deceased was her father.

I took the coffin from the bearers when… Yes, I was sure, it was her and it was difficult not to look. I couldn't help it. But there was no sign of recognition from either of us.

She wouldn't remember me. Why should she? I had been thirteen when she was my music teacher, even though I couldn't read a note. Maybe because I could never take my eyes off her and those American Tan nylons, she just might.

In every lesson after that first flash I wished and wished I could see just once more the top of her nylons and maybe, maybe if God was good to me, a little bit more?

We lowered the coffin into the Village. Pulling up the ropes. I glanced over towards her, she was comforting an older woman, possibly her mother. There were no eyes on me. It was me, hoping there would be.

She was walking back to the cars when the Undertaker came over and, while giving me my tip, asked:

   "Are you Peter Street?"

   "Yes,"

   "Good for you," he said.

That was it. Nothing else. No nod to any of the mourners. Nothing.

Over the years; I asked him a few times who had asked about me, but he never gave me a name, perhaps he didn't know. But

I was sure it was her. Miss Bretherton. Who else could it have been?

The following day the foreman came into the cabin to tell us there was a rush on in the big cemetery. They needed another digger. I volunteered because I wanted to meet the diggers from the other two cemeteries.

Everyone in the cabin laughed when Arnold, pointed to me and said:

"Have grave-digger will travel."

\*\*\*

## Chapter 5

## A Land of Giants

*Heaton Cemetery:*

Grave-diggers' cabin. Two men, one with a boxer's face, were sitting in silence. Even sitting in their chairs both were taller than me. I was in a 'Land of Giants.' Clogs and overalls were on the floor beneath names painted on a lime green wall. As I walked in I was hit with the heavenly smell of bacon cooking alongside onions, chops, liver, sausages, eggs and God knows what else, in a huge iron pan on a black range fired by coals.

"What's the cat brought in this time?" asked the boxer's face. Laughter.

The same guy stood up displaying his fine, full, six-foot two or three frame and introduced himself:

"Bert."

He was the charge hand. The other big guy, who was sat opposite him, had what looked like a solid gold earring, the sort worn by Travellers. I was to learn that this earring could be sold, if needed, to pay for his funeral anywhere in the world.

"Don."

I had never seen anyone so tall. He nodded then leaned back in his chair. Schtum.

I moved some clogs to make space on the wooden bench when the door behind me banged open.

"Are you Street?" a voice boomed.

He didn't give me the chance to nod before he stiffened up, chest out, shoulders back. He talked about me getting my

28

breakfast and how I needed to get more fat on my ribs. His tone
changed becoming softer:

"We have a young girl in. Six-footer."

They talked about a wall falling on her. Instant. Gone.

"Nine years old: no age is it? Million to one chance."


Rick and Arnold had told me all about Mr Bob, the Foreman
here. He was an ex-paratrooper involved in 'Operation Market
Garden' and the 'Battle of Arnhem' and this may have caused
him to act like he did. He had a separate cabin which had a
shaving mirror and three-bar electric fire; it was somewhere to
relax, free from Harold's burnt bacon which reminded him of
bullet holes. He couldn't listen to the diggers boasting about
holidays abroad, especially Europe where he had been taken
prisoner. Traumatic! I knew there had been torture in the war,
but nothing more about Mr Bob was ever even hinted at.
Nevertheless, it was strange seeing someone, even a cemetery
foreman, dressed all in black with razor creased trousers, a
bowler hat and shoes, polished to see your faces in. It was very
odd. A joke? No. Definitely not! Pride.

How he boomed:

"Don took care of the young girl's grandmother nine months
ago."

No one responded.


The iron pan on the fire was applauding more and more as half
a dozen more rashers were thrown into it. A few minutes later,
a breakfast full of everything was pushed onto my knee. Too
nervous to refuse, I forced down the kidneys and fried onions,
and followed everyone else's example, mopped up the juices

with slices of bread greased with butter. Almost finished, I felt more like getting ready for bed rather than digging a grave for a nine-year old girl. The other diggers looked at me as though I had won first prize in an 'Ugly Competition.' I even thought they were going to clap me. Then everything about the wall falling and tragically killing the girl was being repeated. The door snapped open. In stepped an elderly man.

"Good one, Harold," Bert said, lifting up his breakfast plate. I'd never seen anyone who was as bent over as Harold. Arthritis crumpled up his fingers so badly it was a wonder he could clean the cabin and make breakfast for everyone five mornings a week.

The two giants at the table nodded to him.

Again, they talked about the little girl, the tragedy and how her picture had been in the paper.

"Lovely picture," Harold said.

He talked of memories of his days at Folds Road School and how the girl's grandmother had been in his class. He slurped from a pint pot of sweet tea. Lips wiped, he described the grandmother's cracking good looks and how everyone was after her. There were giggles when he told us that he had told her he was a fireman and asked her if he could climb the ladder in her nylons.

This was followed by an uneasy silence.

"Grandmother, passed about nine month ago didn't she?"

Nods. Their faces not moving from their breakfast and I hadn't a clue what was going on.

The conversation changed to me and why I hadn't brought a
boiler suit or something similar. How it was important for me
to wear a hat to cover all of my hair. I wondered why. They
talked more about me needing a hat and why wasn't I
informed? Informed about what? The giant at the table chewed
on his pipe, then smirked.

I felt uncomfortable. It was the way they all looked at me.
Boiler suits were hanging shoulder to shoulder; blue giants
waiting, eager, ready for the day's work, when Don, clog irons
sparking on the stone floor, leaned over me and lifted his boiler
suit off the hook and flopped it over me. A magic show, I
disappeared.
Laughter.
   "Enough," the voice boomed. "He's in enough shit without
you lot making it worse."
Laughter died.
   "Don, you throw back for him."
The giant nodded.
   "And help him with the boiler suit."
Another suck on his pipe and another nod.

Harold helped me fold up and up and up the long legs and
then he tied them up with string and the same with the arms.
Finished. I looked like something between a strung-up turkey
ready for a Christmas table and a scarecrow. Laughter.
The tool shed outside was three maybe four times the size I was
used to, yet there was no room to swing a mouse because of all
the spades, shovels, saws, picks, mattocks and a couple of
industrial water pumps - like those the Fire Brigade use.

Ready for the dig, down on the big slope, when Mr Bob came over, asked if I was OK. I didn't understand why Don and him were nodding to each other, then Mr Bob slipped away for his first funeral of the day. He told Don to keep an eye on me.

On that huge slope, the kind we didn't have at the Bridge cemetery, I began to build the staging at a forty-degree angle. Don nodded his approval.
Three-foot into heavy clay when a trickle of water. Sump dug. Black-brown water ladled into a bucket. A nine-inch slate was stopping me from sinking. Everything was going OK. My wooden sides were fitted in tight, safe.
Four-foot.
There were streaks of blue-purple colloids floating in the black. Stench. Knee high, the grave walls were splitting. Don wasn't there, so much for keeping an eye on me. The sides were loose preventing me from climbing in and out.
I jammed my spade against the wall just how Rick had shown me, if I ever found myself in danger. 'A last resort,' he called it. I tried to be calm.
The wooden sides were now resting at a forty-degree angle. The clay sides were bursting in, knee high. I was in a flushed toilet.
I was about to step up onto my spade and then hopefully lift myself out when there was a loud splutter, a roar of an engine. It was Don.

"Here Peewee," he slid a tube from the water pump down.

"Control the grave. Don't try and climb out or it will pull you down with it."

"What am I supposed to do?"

"Stand to the back."

His head and shoulders were above the grave even with his legs in it. He brought down with him a sledge hammer and some wooden heads. The water pump was splodging out the diarrhoea smelling water, browning the grass around a number of graves.

Don, his long legs at first trapped the sides, to stop them sliding, then he lifted them within an inch of each other and wedged them with the head blocks to prevent anything else sliding down or falling in. He did two sides quickly, making it look so easy. He stretched up, and then lifted himself up the five feet to the ground by the grave.

"See, Peewee. Easy. Now you do the next sides."
I did, and the grave was back to being safe, letting me dig down further. Don pulled out the pump and held his spade out:

"Watch and learn," he said. "When it's in clay like this, you can smooth the bottom out."
It was like someone using a trowel to smooth level a wet concrete floor. He glazed the wet floor with the back of his spade. It looked so good and with all the trauma behind us we climbed out and stepped to one side to admire our work. He lit his pipe and went back to his silence. I smoked a Park Drive cigarette, content.

Mr Bob, marched up towards us. He stood with thumbs down the lining of his black trousers, his chest out. He was now almost in my personal space and without taking his eyes from mine he asked Don how I had done.

I held my breath ready for a rollicking. But sweet-smelling smoke from the giant's pipe wafted past me and Don just nodded.

"Nice."

Mr Bob looked at me briefly and then was off somewhere else. Don shrugged his shoulders, sucked on his pipe and that was it. Nothing else was said. And he had seen the dig, seen how difficult it had been.

I finished the remaining work. Drapes over. Ropes checked, in place. Neat and tidy.

Walking behind Don, my two strides to his one, and there was a strange atmosphere: even when his clogs sparked over the stone floor there was a kind of silence. And for someone so big, it was as if he wasn't there. Yet he was. Bizarre. In a strange way he was there but couldn't be heard; almost like a ghost. Yes, a ghost! He was my ghost. That became my secret nickname for him, 'the Ghost.'

In the cabin, I was expecting to be ridiculed for being too immature and no good for the job, to be teased at the very least. Instead, Harold handed me a freshly made mug of tea and a slice of toast. There were no smiles, no pats on the back. Just Bert, the charge hand, asking,

"Alright, Peewee?"

Everything was alright, that is apart from the stench still in my nose.

Half an hour to the young girl's welcoming. Don and me had made sure everything was just right for her.

Mr Bob, bowler hat in hand, was leading the young girl's cortège. His walk was slow, careful and soldier-like. Fifty yards down the slope from where Don and me were waiting, he turned left, facing us. No emotion, professional.

He waited while she was lifted out. There was something quite perfect about his funeral ways, the best possible. There was just one funeral car. The rest, well, it was a convoy of trucks which were dressed and covered with red and white floral wreaths, more than I had ever seen at one funeral. She was just yards from us. Oddly, the coffin must have been twice the size normally used for a young girl of her age. I was worried the coffin wasn't going to fit, it was so big.

Mr Bob gave us a respectful nod. We took her, easily. But still worried, we hadn't been told it was going to be so big. I took the lead and with foot end first we lowered her into the arms of her grandmother. Like always, we stepped away while relatives said their very best goodbyes. They were throwing in coins and pound notes on top of the coffin along with sand and soil. There was talk of grandmother looking after her, then one of the women said,

"I hope she doesn't spend her money on silly things."
Then, with everyone gone, I was down, slates slotted in place, ready to back fill when two men approached. One of them was just a bit older than me, the other a lot older. He came into my space, grabbed the spade from me. Which was a first for me. I squared up to him.

"Peewee, it's their way." Said Don.

I gave up the spade and followed my Ghost onto the next line of graves where we rested and smoked, until the two men had finished. There was something really sad, more than any other funeral I'd been at before. I could feel my own tears rising. Don nudged me:

"No."

I pulled myself together.

"Travellers, Peewee. Different cultures." Then back to his pipe.

I started talking about the size of the coffin; stunned when Don said it was probably filled up with her dolls, favourite dresses and other personal items. He tapped his pipe, sucked and then amazed me even more when he said:

"I wouldn't be surprised if there were letters and such for grandmother."

We cleaned up and moved the staging.

Back in the cabin. Lunch time with pint pots of tea. Hot dinners cooked in that iron pan. Comic swearing, each one taking the piss out of the other. Banter the like I'd only had before with the Gaff lads. Then, there was a game of dominoes and I was sworn at for doubling up the ends forcing everyone to slap their very secret dominoes onto the table in frustration.

\*\*\*

Later, Sandra and me, enjoyed fish and chips from the West End chippy, which faced the Hen and Chickens pub. She talked about us having a beer at the Hen and Chicken pub. I explained that this, along with certain other town centre pubs, was quite rough. She was OK about this, because she knew I was keeping my word about not seeing any of the Gaffs. We walked towards Spa Road and the Gypsies' Tent pub, which Sandra said she liked because of its old-fashioned black and white facade. Thankfully, I persuaded her not to go in.

Twelve months before in this pub, Phil Mather, his sparring partner Kevin O' Mara and some of the other Gaffs had collected monies in a battered flat cap, to pay for me to be given a blow job by a local 'prossie.' I tried escaping but the guys held me back. Thankfully only seven shillings and six pence could be raised. She looked at me with her dark looks and thinner than thin face, strained under her red hat cocked to one side. I went into panic mode. I honestly thought she was going to accept the money. I shook my head hard.

I had heard about this happening before to young Gaffs with older guys watching whilst virginities were taken. In anticipation there was a silent waiting broken by a few giggles, until she shook her head and said,
"I don't take my teeth out for less than ten bob."
There were arguments over bets lost and won. She downed her drink and quietly walked out. Once out she stumbled down the three or four steps to the main road footpath and away she swayed.
Gypsies' Tent was a No, No!

I hurried Sandra past and onward to the Nevada skating rink. We had talked earlier about going skating but when we got there changed our minds, keeping our promise to save every penny for our mortgage.

\*\*\*

Four days later a six-footer down on the Church of England section came in. Mr Bob almost smiled when he gave me the chit, while telling me our latest had been a long-standing member of a Sally Army brass band. Mr Bob was now smiling. I shrugged my shoulders.

Don was setting up the staging on a slope which was twice the steepness of the last dig for the young girl, but I was OK with it. Even when Bert came down with a pair of Wellingtons I said I was OK - thinking they were just winding me up. Seeing Don wheeling down one of the industrial pumps was when my nerves started to stir. OK, I had an idea we were going into a battle of sorts, but my imagination let me down, I wasn't even close.

Even before I got into the swing of the dig, Mr Bob and Bert kept on coming down to check my progress. My Ghost on the staging was indicating his approval. Then one of them mentioned the deceased's band and the three of them went into fits of laughter. They said I needed to experience the happening, whatever that meant?

Three-foot down, Don took over. Everything was going fine. Five-foot we swapped places. The sides were good. OK, we'd taken out four buckets of water. But it was easy, a good dig.

Five-foot-six and the sides were still good. No problem. I shoved my spade down through the last couple of inches and tapped the top of the coffin beneath. Inexplicably, water gushed up from below, in seconds my clogs were drowned. Feet soaked. Don hurried the pump down; the engine spluttered to life.

Yes, spludge was flying over everything in its range and maybe just that bit further. Bert and Mr Bob came back with mops and buckets to help clean up the headstones and swill the grass to make it as clean as possible. Even Don was surprised with the amount of water now flooding up. He thought we might have hit an underground river that I was now sinking in to. Bert was wheeling down another pump; within minutes he was down in the grave helping and directing. The first pump seemed to be tiring but was still working hard or as much as it could.

The pumps didn't make much difference. and we were concerned that in a couple of hours the funeral was due in. I didn't get it, if they thought there could be a problem why hadn't we started earlier?

Our new member, soon to arrive, had been a Salvation Army member for most of his life. He'd had an important role in leading their brass band. He had grown up and lived with the band, and he had died with the band. So, it was only fitting that the brass band would come and play at his funeral. A first for me. A last for him.

Time was tight, now half an hour before the funeral party
arrived and yet we still had to spludge out a couple of bath-
fulls. Not so bad if that was it.
If only!

With five minutes to go Mr Bob hurried down the road to meet
the cortège. He composed himself, professional, standing
between the cemetery gates, bowler hat in hand, waiting as if
everything was perfect. He then walked his slow, perfected
funeral walk while towing along the party and brass band, who
were holding their gleaming instruments, ready to play any
tune asked of them.

They were two hundred yards away as Don and Bert were
making sure as much water was out as possible. Then Bert
pulled out the pump and dragged it to one side. I helped Don
with the ropes and the box of sand.
Everything was set, it was as perfect as it could be in the
circumstances.

The procession stopped at the top of the path and then about
fifty yards away they lifted the coffin out and were bringing
him down on their shoulders, all the while careful not to slip
and drop him onto the brown sludge (never mind getting
covered in it themselves). Embarrassment wouldn't even come
close. Me and Don put the ropes through the brass rings; we
waited for the band to strike up. Then we lowered him. The
water was flooding up, I followed Don's lead and left the ropes
attached.  About the same time as the coffin started floating
back up the band played: 'Let's All Gather by The River.'

Everyone tried to suppress their laughter. Further planned tunes could not be played. Bert had to walk away. I pinched my sides until they hurt. Mourners' shoulders were heaving up and down with silent laughter. A good time seemed to be had by all.

Service over and the mourners gone. I was standing on staging wondering what to do with a floating and rising coffin which was now half way up the six-foot grave. Bert and Don moved me to one side while they lifted the coffin the last few feet back up onto the staging. Don lit his pipe. Bert pulled on a Woodbine. Mr Bob, taking his time was using a three or four-foot pointed iron bar like a walking stick. I was wondering what was happening, then it suddenly dawned. No, they couldn't?

"Go," Mr Bob said to me, "go and get Harold to put the kettle on."

Half way up the hill, wondering what was happening, I turned. The coffin was back up on the staging then Mr Bob, as though he was in a spook film, stabbed holes into the lid of the coffin. A few stabs later they lowered the colander back down into the sploshing's of a six-foot grave, with not only one but two pipings belonging to the pumps working their guts out to remove what water they could before resting the coffin on top of the one below.

Half an hour later. Slates on. Back filled. Job done. Nothing looked out of place.

\*\*\*

Me and Sandra spent that evening looking through windows of
various estate agents. Our very maximum mortgage with joint
wages would be two thousand pounds. Then Sandra started
talking about babies and losing her wage and asking what
would we do then? At home Dad freaked:

"The working classes don't own houses and don't have
mortgages!"
He talked about us being tied, owned and at the mercy of them,
but how renting would keep us free.
The to-ing and fro-ing about buying or renting lasted all week
and all weekend.

Monday morning in the cabin, I asked for some independent
advice. Don said:

"Simple. If you want to leave your kids something then buy. If
you don't, rent."
Simple? Of course.

\*\*\*

An Asian funeral was due in; four-foot-six on top of the hill.
First one after dinner. With nothing else in, Don came and
helped. The dig was dry, easy. A couple of hours later the job
was done.

"Come on," he said. "We'll go and meet Joe and Tommy who
work the Crematoria"
They weren't much bigger than me. They wore clean sleeves
rolled up above their elbows, even their blue aprons were clean.
They offered me a cigarette which was unusual.

## Hidden Depths – Peter Street

While there were sobs, music, speeches from the other side of the curtain we talked in whispers while waiting impatiently for the coffin to be pushed through the curtain. Then off the fancy slide it was lifted onto steel rollers. Our mood was good. It all somehow reminded me of the bakery where I worked after leaving school. It was the way Joe and Tommy took the coffin like some large tray of uncooked loaves which were then shoved into the oven. It seemed they could have been bakers.

Don took me round the back of the ovens where he pointed for me to look through the peep hole. Spook movie time, the way the coffin disappeared. I am certain that body moved and then lifted up a foot or so, only to then to melt into nothing.

I felt uncomfortable watching bones being crushed into a large bowl, mixed up with maybe a couple dozen or so other folk who were then shovelled into a wheelbarrow only to be buried in a communal grave.
The work of the spooks kept me awake that night.

Next day, after lunch, a first for me, the Asian funeral with no women attending. Just dozens and dozens of men carrying the coffin up above their heads while other members were trying their best to touch the coffin.

It brought memories of Burden Park and being lifted and passed above all the adults. Safe, behind the nets with all the other kids while watching, Bolton Wanderers v. Wolves: 1957 quarter finals of the F.A. cup.

## Hidden Depths – Peter Street

A new digger was due to start shortly at Heaton and then I
would be asked to go back home to Bridge cemetery.

During my last few days there, me and Don were to share a
seven-foot-six dig. Fine. Four-foot down, my brain seemed to
change speed, then direction, backwards. I couldn't stop myself
from putting the Captain Web match in my mouth and striking
my Park Drive on the fag box. From then on, I was in automatic
mode.

Don wouldn't have known the signs of a grand mal seizure.
Apparently, he came down, grabbed my overalls by the chest
and leg, and then just lifted me up and out. It was an
ambulance job. The hospital bed sheets were covered in mud.
Trying to move brought pain. Pain as though elephants had
walked all over me. Eventually I managed to move. Bending
down I forced my eyes under the bed where my clogs were
coated in mud and my bloody tongue felt like it was in shreds.

Four days later I trod into the cabin and was met with Silence.
Harold placed a breakfast on my knee. I was waiting for all the
sorries and 'Why didn't you tell us, we didn't know what to
do?'
That was the usual, but gravediggers are anything but usual. A
room full of nods were aimed at me and that was it. Yes, it had
been my first grand mal while I was a digger. It had also been a
first for them and, like at the Bridge, they had passed with
flying colours. It was then I knew more than ever, I was one of
them and truly accepted.

## Chapter 6

## The Logbook

*Weekend.*

First stop: Graham Balls Estate Agents on Bradshawgate, where we eyed a semi just off Church Road at £2,000. It was exactly what we wanted. All right it may have been out of our range, it was the excitement of going to look at our very first three-bedroom house.

Half an hour or so after a guided tour we were sitting in the bus shelter at the bottom of Ivy Road where we talked money. Sandra worked out we would need a £300 deposit, but it was all becoming too much for me. So, she took charge of everything to do with numbers including money, bills: the lot. Mum had taught me from an early age (she dreamed about me becoming a Catholic priest) about cooking both English and traditional Irish cooking; it's why Sandra jobbed me with everything to do with food. Everything sorted in that huge bus shelter we cuddled and carried on with our wedding dreams.

\*\*\*

*The Gypsies Tent.*

Johnny Kitson walked in holding a rolled up a newspaper, one he'd never read. When we hugged, he slipped the log book I needed into my pocket. He still looked like he hadn't two pennies to rub together. We talked both good and bad times. He was still in the big money, with his sixpence-a-go stall which years ago I helped him start up, I don't think anyone had ever won any of the stacks of prizes on offer. To win, punters

45

had to throw a ping-pong ball into a soup dish without it bouncing out. I was one of only a handful who knew the secret of the game.

We were hugging our goodbyes, when he reminded me how everything was an illusion. But this time there was something different about the way he said 'illusion', like he was on his way out, or I would never see him again. I began to feel tearful and of course I asked.
He didn't reply.
Before leaving he handed me a note he didn't want me to look at.

"If you ever need me ring that number. Anything, do you hear?"
He again stressed: 'Anything.'
I didn't reply but pocketed the note.
In all our years......there was something he wasn't sharing. We said our goodbyes and that was it. Gone. I was always jealous of him, but never told him.

***

It was both satisfying and welcoming to see the green cast iron gates of the Bridge something magical. Of course, it was my mind, off on some other planet, but I couldn't help thinking they were there for me as if I was some country leader or general inspecting the troops. I was home. Safe.

Elbows, Woodbines, mugs of tea, all on the cabin table. Rick nodded, Arnold gave me a weak smile. Sam nodded between sleeps. That was it. Nothing much was asked about my days at Heaton, the big cemetery, not even my thoughts about Mr Bob, or digging in floods of water in seriously heavy clay.

Disappointment kicked in. At the very least they could have asked? Rick broke the silence by saying not much had happened at the Bridge.
I said nothing.

Fags were pulled on. And I was changing into my digging gear when the foreman came in; at least he asked my thoughts of the big cemetery. But that was it.

I couldn't help being a bit upset. I had had and survived real traumas, and they, Rick and Arnold, well, they had just been doing bits of this and that around a small cemetery. Easy. Not like the one I had been in with an ex sergeant who had survived Arnhem, not forgetting a six-foot ghost and Bert the charge-hand who all helped to keep me safe. All right, in my frustration I wanted to freak, and yes it was difficult keeping all my freaks under one roof so to speak.

I really didn't mean to slam the door on my way out. It just sort of happened. Arnold was right behind me, so too was Rick and the Foreman. They stood back waiting.
In the tool shed a sou'wester hat and kiddies' life-belt attached to a rope swung down from the rafters, smacking me in the face.

Laughter. The welcome back kicked off in a big way with free fags and a bottle of booze. OK, it wasn't exactly party time, but close enough. There were questions and thoughts about Mr Bob.

Surprises all round: Mr Bob being like a dad, Don an older brother and Bert the life guard.

Me and Rick were to share opening a new nine- footer again on the Church of England section. Arnold was shaking his head. There was an ominous silence. Everybody knew it was sand!

"Again," warned Arnold, "all sand."

"Bloody hell!" was all I could say.

It was a Romany dig. Luckily, we had been given a week's warning. Before giving us the chit, he asked if we were going to be all right. There was no-one else, so we couldn't say 'No' could we?

Comforting, well kind of, knowing Arnold would keep an eye on us. He also reminded us it was going to be a vault and all the sand would be taken away, so thankfully there would be no back filling, as the floor and sides were to have brick walls for sides.

"Bloody Hell," me again.

A dumper truck had been hired for the job of taking the sand away. Double work for us. There were tensions all round. Late afternoon.

Rick, remembering our last experience with sand, teased me about matches and lighters. Arnold was walking toward us with ropes and a ladder. He threw the lot on the tarmac in front of the grave.

No one said anything for a while.

Each of us smoked our own cigarettes. Gathered our own thoughts. Time. Rick and Arnold took off the marble top paving. Sand. There was sand all along its nine-foot length. Arnold took charge:

"Rick will be with you all the while."

Serious.

"The first creaking and you get out. No lighting fags first. It's out you get and out you stay, until we see what's happening." I wasn't sure if Arnold was making my nerves better or worse. My first spade, a full spit down without any real pressure. Easy. A dream after the hard slog in that heavy clay of Heaton, a dead sodden earth which needed cutting into cubes each time, slow, heavy. Yet, you could take an eye off it. Relax. Well sort of. OK, it tested me, but in a way to give me enough clear warning and time to get in the blocks.

Safe.

Five-foot.

A dream dig! Sand, easy. Rick was helping by putting the sides in. Resting, fags going. I was sitting on my spade shooting-stick-fashion when the sand pulled. Silly I know, but the grave seemed to sigh like it was alive. Then it grabbed and pulled my clogs down just below my shins. Rick handed me down a slate to firm my standing and asked if I was OK? Creaking. It was shifting. Sand! I was about to climb up the wooden sides.

"No!" shouted Arnold. "You'll bring the lot down on you."

A ladder came sliding down:

"Use it."

He didn't need to tell me twice.

"Up you come."

49

The three of us waited for something to happen. Nothing.
A tease, testing us!
Three mugs of tea and five fags later the grave seemed calm.
No creaking.
Jacket off. Arnold, sleeves rolled up showing his tattoos (Rick
thought they were Royal Marine Commando ones). The ladder
eased him down into the grave. He was firm on the slate, his
ear pressed against the wooden sides like one of those old-
fashioned doctors, listening, bending down and grabbing a
handful of sand.
It was almost funny watching sand sift through his fingers like
a kiddie's first time on the beach.  Silly I know but surely the
grave shuddered? My imagination of course.
The ladder climbed him back up, out on to the opposite side of
the path. Between pulls on our cigarettes, we had a serious
discussion about carrying on or waiting for some support. It
came down to the same answer/ question - what support? The
Fire Brigade? We laughed at the thought. That was it. There
was no support, we had no other option.

Arnold walked over to the grave, took a last pull on his fag,
flicked it away and let the ladder slowly take him back down.
There was something calm about him, cool, almost respectful,
while he pressed his full hand, patted each of the sides, then
turned his attention to the foot and head blocks. Was there
something we didn't know? Back with us he took out and
smoked one of his Woodbines.
  "No more tonight, cover it over."
That was it. He said nowt else, there was some secret he wasn't
for sharing.  Back in the cabin, where elbows shared the table

with mugs of tea, ash trays, fag packets, matches and the odd lighter, Arnold broke the silence,

"How would we feel if some big heavy clogs stepped on us?"
We were puzzled by the question.
He nodded at us.

"It's all right you two laughing!"
That was it. All very odd.
Sandra and me spent the evening looking through windows of estate agents. She talked money and how we would have a better chance for a mortgage if we saved with a Building Society. In the town centre there was something warming about looking, pointing through the windows of Boardman's Furniture store. We planned and dreamed about colours and sizes, what went with what and how it would fit into our very first house.

I walked Sandra home and then caught the last bus home. I really didn't mean to cause an argument, but I just forgot myself, probably due to my excitement of being with Sandra. It was the simplest of things, I mentioned to Dad that we were going to put £5 down on a twin-tub washing machine. That was it. Nothing more. But it all kicked off, about us even thinking about buying a washing machine. Again, it was all a class thing and how they managed with next to nothing in Dad's time. Just being the two of us, why could we not, for the time being, manage with a Dolly tub?
Mum came hurrying into the front room, wondering what all the fuss was about. She was horrified at the thought of a Dolly tub even being mentioned, never mind us actually buying one! I

called time and went to bed. Mum followed me. In my bedroom, she whispered:

"You get your washing machine, you'll need it."

She gave me £20, £5 for the down payment, the rest towards the final payment.

I gave Sandra the money the following day.

\*\*\*

In the morning our first job was to lift the huge double-door cover from off the grave. Rick was front man, Arnold at the back.

"One, two, three."

The dark was prised open.  The bottom set of sides had disappeared. The grave floor seemed higher than when we had left it, but it seemed alright.  Arnold told me and Rick it was OK. But it wasn't that easy. Saying that, Arnold was down already. He was sinking in a very different kind of sand. Powdery. Arnold carried on digging with no worries. Bizarrely, a foot down a wooden side appeared, already in place, perfect. Obviously the missing one. It was still making us wonder about this dig and ask ourselves what was going to happen next? What to do next was really getting to me. I asked Rick and he handed me a cig. We didn't have a light so hurried the few steps over to Arnold who was squatting and pulling on a Woodbine.

"What's up with you two sissies?"

Arnold stayed down and finished the dig.

Five days to the funeral and the bricklayers for the vault came in. That morning I was sent to The Old Tonge Cemetery, set back off Bury Road. *Wednesday morning:*

Johnny Kitson kept in the shadows a few yards away from me at the Sally-Up-Steps' chippy, Chorley Old Road. I had Johnny's forged Log book (I didn't ask questions). I waited on the edge of the kerb - just how we had practised - "an old Gaffs' blag," he said, "worked every time." Nervous I waited for a wagon, any wagon, hoping that when I held up the log book the driver would see one of his own, and would stop and ask me where I wanted to go. At least that was the plan.

The fourth wagon was a 1958, 957 Commer. The driver leaned across, asked where I was going. Before I could answer he asked to see the log book which I had forgotten to shove in my pocket. My answers weren't making sense, so Johnny stepped out of the shadows. No blagging. He just explained the problem of me needing to save money for my wedding. No more questions; the driver helped me up into the wagon and took me within a five-minute walk to the cemetery. The same driver gave me a lift every morning from then on.

\*\*\*

## Chapter 7

### Bessemer

Of course, there were always fears about my epilepsy when meeting new work mates. Though it had been three years since these fears had last surfaced. Three years since the bike I had saved my paper money for, was taken from me. The bike I had shared with girls, giving them piggyback rides. Great, until my parents took it all away and, can you believe it, gave it away to 'a good home?' The dreams of the Triumph Tiger Cub Motorbike had all but ended, gone, along with all my biker friends. Not only that, but I had been sacked from my first job in the bakehouse after having a seizure. Then it was the paper-mill, sacked. The warehouse, sacked. The butchers and slaughterhouse, sacked! Apart from Sandra and the Gaffs, I had been friendless for three years. Yes, there were big fears.

A cobbled road walked me between two stone pillars into Tonge cemetery. The diggers' cabin was on the far left, and the door was open. There were no smells of bacon, no cooking, no ash trays, no overalls hanging from hooks, no clogs. The place was spotless. There was even a couple of dozen or so books on wall shelves. The digger, Joe, didn't take his eyes from the book he was reading. His hand didn't let go of his breakfast bottle of Guinness. He was no more than five-foot and almost as broad as he was tall.

"You're Peewee then?" he said without looking up. "Have you dug in Bessemer before?"

"Bessemer, what's Bessemer?" I replied.

In the cabin on the stone flagged floor, he suggested I make a pot of tea. The sugar and tea were in their own caddies, fresh milk was in the fridge. There were choices of butters, margarine, jams and marmalades and there was fresh bread. Book down, he looked relaxed. It seemed the right time to tell him about my epilepsy.

"You have fits. So what?"

With that he went back to his Guinness.

He voiced his disappointment at not being offered a hot drink.

"Always ask, it's important." He stressed the 'important.'


Clogs on, I was ready when Jimmy walked in. Not much older than me, twenty-three, maybe twenty- four. Gravedigger by day, club bouncer/doorman at one of the most notorious Bolton night clubs by night. He nodded, first at me, then at Joe.

"Peewee," said Joe pointing at me.

Jimmy, before sitting at the table with his rolled-up newspaper and before making himself a coffee, asked if I had had a hot drink that morning?

"Yes, thank you."

I think they were smiling at my politeness.

"Peewee," said Joe pointing at me. "Has fits?"

Jimmy asked about warning signs. They eased when I said there was always about an hour's warning. Joe asked if I could drive. They both glared at me when I said I couldn't. Hadn't. Not allowed to. Jimmy wanted to know what 'allowed' had to do with it? My thoughts turned to all the restrictions placed on me. They started talking about how the cemetery was on private property. Maybe it was me, but everyone, and I mean everyone, had said I couldn't drive under any circumstances

and now… well all of that was being knocked on the head.
Especially when Joe told me I would have to drive on this site.
I was gob smacked.

Jimmy explained how the tractor only had a top speed of ten
miles an hour. And the way he said, "you'll have a hard job
killing anyone," made us all laugh.

Between giggles I tried talking about driving licences. They
brushed it aside. That was it, all my fears had just melted away.
Regardless of who or what I was, as long as I could dig graves
and drive their little tractor I was in. OK, it was only a little
tractor but my god, I was going to drive! There was no escaping
it, I was one of them… family!

Joe wanted to know more about Sandra.

How did he know about Sandra?

I said nowt.

They both wanted to know how long I'd been digging and
why?

I explained.

 They said it was better being open about family matters and
that working for the Council more or less guaranteed a
mortgage.   Joe closed his book, grabbed his heavy woollen
jumper from his chair and put it on. While walking out of the
cabin he was ripping off dangling bits of wool from his sleeves
and indicated for me to follow him.

We went in the double size garage/tool shed where there was a
long wooden bench, clear of all tools. On the walls to my left
were spades, shovels, picks, mattocks and the like, all in their
own proper place.  He pulled his jumper off from over his huge

chest and laid it down on the bench, its arms stretched,
sprawled out like a spatchcock chicken. He took the axe from its
place on the wall and, without warning, chopped off the sleeves
of the jumper just above elbow level.

"That's better," he said, whilst pulling it back over his head.
He slotted the axe back into its place on the wall.
He took me to the back of the shed, pointed to a pneumatic
jackhammer and asked if I had ever used one.

"Why?"

He asked again. I'd never seen one, never mind used one.
He gave me a wry smile, patted the motor end of the drill.
Good boy. Another wry look and he smiled,

"You will."

He led me into the garage next to the shed where we pushed
out a tiny two-stroke engine tractor and trailer.
 Jim was coming out of the cabin and shouted in a matter of fact
way:

"Let Peewee drive it."

I was dumb struck.

Yes, they'd been told about my epilepsy. So why were they
standing there, arms across chests, as though they knew the
wool was being pulled over their eyes with the log book thing.
Joe even asked me how long my epilepsy had been stopping me
from driving. Of course, it was aimed at the log book thing.
Bugger.

Joe gave me a determined look. Jimmy was smiling. Then he
explained he needed me and the tractor to get to know each
other, something to do with emergencies. Then he asked if I
really knew about Bessemer?

I shrugged.

He gave a knowing look and said:

"Bessemer feeds on coffins, just eats them away, gone before you know it."

Then with a smirk on his face added:

"Some, for whatever reason, weren't slated on top."

I looked at him puzzled.

Then they realised I hadn't a clue. They talked about a Johnny Foster. I'd never heard of Johnny Foster. They looked sympathetically at me and talked about him not returning after the second day.

They didn't mean to frighten me, did they? They then said something about 'right up to his chin.' Joe was repeating how he had told this Johnny Foster until he was blue in the face, how he had warned and warned him, but he had chosen not to listen. That was their version of it all. They went into deep conversation about that part of the cemetery, and then they turned to me:

"Peewee, look out for the last few inches. Keep your feet on the rim of the coffin below and hold the spade sideways when you're not digging."

I said nothing.

He went on to say the bones are never affected, only the coffin. Back in the shed, we loaded a two to three-foot long jackhammer together with its chisels and hammers, not forgetting lengths of pneumatic piping, onto the miniature trailer. The jackhammer was cold, strong, muscular even. I'd never heard of Bessemer before, never mind dug in it. It seems it was waste from an iron foundry, buried here years ago. We set the staging at a huge fifty maybe sixty-degree slant.

In turn, we took off the top soil. Jimmy took over and connected up the jackhammer and all its bits. He took me through all of its dangers and was insistent I wore gloves. He didn't know why himself, just something he'd heard. Something he didn't really understand but had something to do with 'White-finger' and shaking. Even though he went through everything he then told me we might not use the jackhammer, at least not on the dig that day.

Again, it was something I had to learn, all to do with what to do in an emergency. My first grave in the old cemetery and we were going down seven-foot-six in Bessemer on the Church of England section. It was an old grave, originally a twelve-footer. Jimmy broke the silence, again insisting I did everything exactly as he said.

Until that time me and machinery were a complete no-no for everyone from Mum and Dad, teachers to Mrs Jones the Youth Employment Officer. The diggers were OK with it once they knew all about the hour warning I have before an epileptic seizure. Jimmy was standing with his arms across his chest. He didn't need to say anything, the look he gave me said that grave-digging was life itself. The rules seemed to be simple: equality, trust, teamwork, and safety. Epileptic driving, jackhammers, safety - apart from the Gaffs, this was a first freedom for me. I knew this was not the norm. Then again, gravediggers are not the norm! Jimmy, handed me the jackhammer, gave me another wry smile and he said:

"This will be easy for you especially after driving a big old 957 Commer wagon."

He obviously knew I was blagging about that and he was letting me know he did.

It was late Wednesday morning in the Church of England section when Jimmy pointed for me to climb on to the tractor and drive it all the way back to our cabin. My excitement was obvious. He was to walk alongside, while I kept it in first gear. All the way up, past some of the oldest graves, past even the 'Nutter' gravestone, up and past the main gate and manager's house, finally into the yard.

Lunch time in the cabin with mugs of tea we talked families and played cards for matches. They teased me again about Sandra.

Lunch time over. We were back down ready for the afternoon dig. We talked easily. Then it was my first kick, with a round mouth spade, into Bessemer, tiny bits of lunar-like-clinker - like I was digging into the moon. Deeper down, the grave was nowhere near as strong as the usual clay or even sandy grave. And it stank of sulphur. I could also smell the sweat of the diggers who had worked on this before me. Diggers who'd hammered and wedged, clinked out the twelve-foot deep coffin shape through this cold volcanic-like rock. My dig had been a lifetime easier than the others, but now I could feel clammy sweat on my skin.

Resting, I went to pull on a Park Drive, relaxed. I forgot about the warnings. I was standing on the middle of the coffin when Jimmy started to shout something about keeping my spade sideways when without warning, a kind of trap-door just dropped me down, down up to my waist. Jimmy leaned in and grabbed hold of my hand to stop me from dropping completely. Things were happening around my legs. Yes, there were bones, but there was something else. I didn't want to know what else. I just wanted out!

Back in the cabin. OK. They offered me sweet tea. Fags. Joe even offered his last bottle of Guinness to take my mind off the happening. They asked about Sandra. It was one of my weakest moments, and that's why I confessed to them about wanting to take her to Blackpool for a weekend, but her parents had insisted on a note from the landlady about us having separate rooms.

They didn't respond at first.

I was still getting over the shock of the drop, when Jimmy came up with the idea: choose a guest house, visit it on a day outing and ask the owners for one of their letterheads. Joe and Jimmy started talking about the wording of the letter for Sandra's strict parents. Fear and shock was now replaced with thoughts about Sandra, me and Blackpool.

Back on the morning dig. The funeral, backfill and tidied-up, it all went perfectly. Home.

\*\*\*

Sandra loved the idea of us spending our very first weekend away together. No parents. No one telling us what we could or couldn't do. Not only that, but we were starting to plan our life together.

Friday. My first chit with 'pauper' written in red ink on a smaller than normal piece of paper. No surname, just 'Alex.'

Jimmy had helped with the four-foot six dig but this one he
wanted me to do on my own. Everything had also been
arranged with the Undertaker, so that was it, alone! I was
frightened, I'd never been trusted to do anything alone before,
and I remembered with growing uneasiness that the gravedigger is always in charge. Gulp!

Myself and the Undertakers hovered around the grave like
relatives.  The priest splashed some Holy Water onto the coffin
then moved to the opposite side of the grave to throw in a
handful of sand and soil. Jimmy later helped with the backfill.
Done. Tidied up, done. We then walked around the cemetery
picking just one flower from each of the fresh bouquets and
made our own wreath and gave some life to a very dead grave
and said our own farewells to 'Alex.'

\*\*\*

*Monday Morning.*
Both Jimmy and Joe commented about me looking pleased with
myself. They laughed when I showed them two letterheads
from 'Phoenix Guest House,' Blackpool, which me and Sandra
had visited on Saturday.  They made me coffee in a big mug
and I told them about my day trip to Blackpool with Sandra.
I've never been able to explain why I felt I could trust them with
anything, everything! Even my future!

We shared wording for the fake letter. Joe even talked about
Rhyl, and how he knew some guest house owners in River
Street and how he might be able to do a deal for us there, if
Blackpool didn't work out. Jimmy talked memories about

weekends in River Street spent with his girlfriends. Me and Joe were laughing when Tommy, the manager of the cemetery, walked in and then handed Jimmy a chit. Tommy asked me how the weekend went. Before I could answer he started telling us about the June of '56 when he first took his girlfriend for a weekend away to Number One, John Street, Rhyl. He closed his eyes and with a deep breath:

"Pat Boone was in the top ten."

Back in the land of now he said:

"There's unbroken Bessemer down near the Nuns' section." said Tommy, "Peter will be with you."

Looks hit me hard. Outside in the cabin we loaded up the jackhammer bits, spades, mattocks and a wheelbarrow. I asked why the wheelbarrow? But he never said. Once in the driver's seat I shoved it in first gear. Jimmy came out of the cabin with a first aid box and a bottle of water. This would be my first 'hard' Bessemer and Jimmy warned that once through the layers of Bessemer, it would likely be flooded, not just wet. Jimmy explained:

"Always has been on that section"

We were also going to be digging about a hundred yards from the 'Lion Tamer!'

Walking alongside the tractor Jimmy kept a straight face while telling me all about Thomas MacCarte, Lion Tamer. MacCarte had been too drunk to remember to chew on his plug of tobacco which helped him to control the lion. The other digger Joe was insistent I learned all about the Lion Tamer. He even wrote it all down on an A4 piece of paper. He made me learn it parrot fashion, so I would be prepared for doing guided tours around

63

the cemetery, for those interested in the various graves and, particularly, the story of a drunken one-armed lion tamer. Apparently, the story goes that the lion tamer went into the town centre of Bolton dressed as a gladiator, poking a toy sword at the lion,

On or near the anniversary of the Lion Tamer having his head ripped off, people dressed as 'gladiators' could be seen down the side of the Nuns' Section practising sword skills. Yes, difficult to believe, but Joe would swear it was the truth, these 'gladiators' did exist. Wild! Joe was right about keeping a straight face. As I told them the story, I found keeping a serious face difficult but just about managed to do so, and the gladiators gave me the usual two-shilling tip. Joe called tips our 'bread and butter stuff' and if it wasn't forthcoming, he told me to cough a certain way, into my hand, until a tip materialised.

Back to the grave, me and Jimmy took it in turns to take off the top soil. Then Bessemer, we hit it big time. Jimmy fixed up the jackhammer and began to teach me how to use it while keeping safe. His whole body was shaking while trying to hammer through the steely clinker. My turn, he pointed down:

"Let the hammer do all the work, just find a seam and go from there."

Easy-peasy.

Aye, until I started trying to hammer through iron. Twenty minutes and I hadn't even drilled out a spade-full. We rested, drew on fags. Jimmy explained that there were no sides while we were in Bessemer, but as soon as we hit clay, trouble. Big, wet, stinking trouble!

64

## Hidden Depths – Peter Street

Jimmy was down on his knees, gangster-like, 'Machine Gun Jimmy.' Firing, filling that head section full of holes. Jackhammer down, he swung that mattock brutally, causing his arms, body and the mattock itself to vibrate violently. Solid as solid could be. Nothing was happening. Then one more swing and that mattock went all out and pulled a slice of the section down, perfect. Jimmy looked up, gave me a wry smile, shrugged his shoulders. More, brutal, mattock meets Bessemer, angry with splashing sweat from his vibrating body. For those few seconds Bessemer was winning. Jimmy head down, determined. jackhammered more holes. He straightened, arms hanging off. He climbed out.

My turn to start drilling away more Bessemer then spade those bits out. I felt a sudden change come over my whole body. I was now mean, a gangster like Jimmy. I was down on one knee firing away. Then the jackhammer's piping snapped away snaking all around me, I don't know how or why it missed me, but thankfully it did and both pipe and jackhammer completely died. Jimmy leaned in and helped me climb out.
 We pulled on Park Drives.

  "Bloody Hell."

  "Aye," he replied. "That's the third time I've seen that."
 We had another silent fag before he asked if I was all right. Of course, I was shaken. I was trying to think about Sandra and that weekend in Blackpool. We had won a blue wall clock at Bingo and we swore we would put it on the kitchen wall in our very first house. I escaped in my day-dreams to as many beautiful places as I could, another galaxy, anywhere away

from Bessemer and jackhammers. Free! Five minutes more and then it would be Jimmy's turn. I nodded.

"Maybe another foot," he said, "then it's clay and water."
It was a good guess!

\*\*\*

*Carl*

Winter and a lot of elderly people had died of Flu at the same time and needed to be buried. Many of the funerals seemed to be using Heaton Cemetery and this was the reason I was sent there from Astley Bridge whilst Carl, a grave-digger I didn't know, was brought in from Tonge.

My brown paper carrier bag was falling apart because of the weight of my muddy clogs & overalls. I was struggling to carry it as well as my flask of scotch broth and the bread wrapped in its Warburtons grease proof paper.

Carl arrived just after me and I took an instant liking to him, I'm not sure why. Maybe because he was the complete opposite to me. He carried his clean clogs in his hands. He wore slacks and had clean shoes. His black hair was swept back from his face. He took off his glasses, wiped them, looked over at me: "So, you're Peewee?" he changed from his Bolton accent to a deep Al Jolson voice saying, "good to meet you." Me and the other diggers were laughing when Mr Bob walked in. Everyone was looking at me when Mr Bob said,
" You're with Carl."

The wooden stagings for two graves had been set up waiting for us in the Church of England section about hundred yards up from the cabin. We set about digging both of them, one after

66

the other. One was a four-foot-six, the other a six-footer and we had no problems with either. Except that Carl was a very funny man and kept making me laugh with his quips and jokes. I stopped digging from time to time due to fits of laughter, even looking at Carl made set me off. I never saw him angry. He was one of those guys who seem to have a permanent smile on his face.

In the hut I was told that Carl was going to be singing at the Pigeon Club in Bridgeman Street on the Saturday, So I thought,
    "Why not go to it?"
Sandra wasn't that keen on going but agreed to eventually. We arrived early and sat fairly near to the stage. The first half of the show was an ordinary 'turn'. But, in the second half Carl came on with a blacked-up face, white lips and white gloves – he looked the spit of Al Jolson and I already knew he had the voice.

"Mammy!" was his first song and it just went on from there. He was superb. Even Sandra clapped enthusiastically. We waited for him after the show, to say hello and introduce him to Sandra. As he came out the remaining audience applauded.
"Hello Peewee," he said.
"Sandra this is…" I started to say
"It's Peter." interrupted Sandra sternly.
Carl corrected himself and from then on all the diggers called me Peter or Pete.

***

We had a nine-footer down on the Catholic section. It was an easy dig in grey loam. The funeral procession arrived, and the bearers had the coffin on their shoulders.

67

"Here we go and don't laugh," Carl whispered in his Jolson voice. I somehow managed to control the giggles. Everything was going well until, as we began lowering the coffin having put the rope through the brass rings, two rings broke and the coffin fell into the grave landing upright. The lid slid partly off and an arm hung out.

"If he wasn't dead before, he's dead now!" Carl whispered to me. That was it, my giggles took over and as the service carried on, though I tried my very best, I couldn't stop them.

I think my disability may have stopped them from sacking me but word came from the boss that Carl would never work with me on a funeral again.

\*\*\*

## Chapter 8

## Exhuming the Welsh Tabernacle

*Astley Bridge Cemetery, late Spring 1969.*

Rick and Arnold said together:

"It's the wandering minstrel!"

Never before had I been greeted with cheers. Even Sam stayed awake long enough to make me a mug of tea. Jimmy and Joe were terrific. My time with them couldn't have been better. Even so, it was a relief being back on home soil. Alright there was going to be sinking sand and stenches far beyond any reasonable nose. There again, mine isn't a reasonable nose, mine is a gravedigger's nose, different, professional. With my mug of tea came a large plate piled high with breakfast food, whilst there was teasing about me dropping through the coffin. Teasing whenever I went to the toilet as they would shout: 'He's gone shaking hands with Sandra's wedding present!' They teased about that bloody jackhammer, and how the air pipe snapped free in its attempt to escape my clumsy hands. Laughter.

Rick lifted up his mug of tea in a toast:

"But he's still here."

With that the rest of the workers lifted their mugs of tea and toasted me. Me!

There were nods and more nods. Sam, forgetting he had already made me a hot drink, asked me again.

Laughter.

Not wanting to upset him I said,

"Please, I'd love a hot drink."

"Make it yourself, idle young bugger."

More laughter.

While the others brought their own news and adventures to the table, Sam fell asleep. Rick took the fag from Sam's already burnt fingers. Everyone and everything was how it was, how it should be.

Rick and me spent the day going around clearing up recently closed up graves, taking off dead wreaths and levelling up the sunken ones with top soil and slates. Round the back of the church we smoked fags, while Rick started telling me about the Romany funeral I had missed. He told me that there were about two, maybe three hundred people who had come in traditional gypsy caravans and trucks and wagons of all sizes. The police had to come over to manage the traffic. Rick giggled while telling me he had never seen shire horses at a funeral before. We moved down towards the Catholic section where he asked my thoughts about exhuming the Welsh Tabernacle. The last internment there had been carried out in 1863.

"What?"

He asked if I was going to the meeting?

"Meeting, what meeting?"

"One week's pay per day of exhuming."

He scanned me. Secretive, nervous, I thought 'No! Definitely Not!' My imagination was getting the better of me. Maybe I'd watched too many spooky films? He leaned into me:

"We've all volunteered; it's what the big wigs want."

I needed to know more but we both continued quietly smoking. Finally, he told me that it was all about trust and being part of a team.

## Hidden Depths – Peter Street

"Grave-digging is all about watching out for each other."
Well, I considered myself part of the team and realised it would
do wonders for our house deposit. So, I replied;
  "Yes, I'm in."
Of course, there was a problem, exhuming! He asked me
questions about my nerves. I wasn't sure what he meant.
My imagination started to take over again, especially when he
talked about lead coffins. I joked about it being safe as we
couldn't crash through lead lids. He forced a smile. I didn't
know it then, but he was preparing me for the worst, preparing
me for something I could never actually imagine. Yes, he had
lifted bodies up before. Where or when he wouldn't go into.
Yes, I was bothered when he said,
  "No, you won't crash through a lead coffin and you wouldn't
want to." He wouldn't go further than that. I pushed and
pushed, but there was no response. No, nothing except:
  "You're with us now."
He gave me one of his Park Drive's, did one of his fancy Zippo
tricks before lighting us.
By the way he shifted to one side, I knew there was something
he wasn't saying. Again, more pushing, but nothing. For
whatever reason he wasn't for spilling the beans. He kept
avoiding my eyes, glancing over my shoulder instead. He knew
what we were going into and said there had to be eight of us. I
needed to know where?
  "The Welsh Tabernacle, round the back of Podmore's Garden
Centre on Deansgate." explained Ricky.  He said it again,
  "Exhuming the Welsh Tabernacle."
I felt he still wanted to tell me something else but wouldn't, so I
honestly didn't have a clue about exhumations.

We were due to start late Spring. All the other diggers had already agreed, I felt I couldn't say "no."
I thought this was going to impress Sandra. Over and over in my mind I kept thinking this was the chance we had been waiting for. Of all things, exhuming could sort our future.

To say Sandra hit the roof would be a massive understatement. I explained the team thing, but she still wasn't happy about me seeing the things she imagined would be there. She thought it would be bad for my epilepsy. Yes, even though she knew I had never had friends like these diggers. Not even the Gaffs could come up to their standard of friendship. But, although we were saving hard, as well as our deposit there were the legal fees which would be at least £50, we needed more cash. Sandra started scanning the Bolton Evening News for part time jobs.

***

*June.*
The word came through, exhuming was to begin that weekend. Sandra wanted to see where and what we would be exhuming. We took a walk down Deansgate, cut thorough Ridgeway Gates, then left into Dukes Alley where old wooden doors, of every colour possible, were standing shoulder to shoulder in a square about half the size of a football pitch. We tried finding gaps to peep through but there were none. It was just old doors, the sort you saw at house demolition sites.

***

*First Exhuming Day*
Saturday morning, I met Bert and Don, the Ghost, outside the Market Hall. Rick, Jimmy, Arnold and Joe were already there.

There was only Carl, the Al Jolson impersonator, to come. Inside five minutes I had hit two Park Drives. Five minutes later we were all there, the full team of eight! We all shook hands.

Carl explained that he, along with some other Council workers, had been lifting and smashing some of the old gravestones lying them flat on the floor. A JCB had been used to take off some of the top soil.

Inside the site there was one large caravan, time and weather had almost rubbed out its green and white colours. Inside eight chairs were squeezed around a Formica table. There was a tiny sink with a small cube of soap hardly big enough to wash one pair of hands never mind eight, and there was no hot water. There were chemical toilets and two small bottles of disinfectant for spraying our overalls. And, get this, there were no masks.

Archaeologists from the local museum wore masks and white overalls. But none for us!

We sat between smokes, teas and coffees talking tactics. Rick nodded. Arnold smiled a strange kind of smile and we all looked at each other. I didn't fully understand what was happening, but they assured me I'd be OK and then there was a short pause before Bert shouted:

"Let's get on."

First, we helped spray each other with disinfectant to try and kill every known thing and maybe a few more, like our emotions and guilt. I also slipped on the rubber gauntlet type gloves, while the others refused them.

Strange how we, the team of eight, were just standing there like mannequins. Rick shook his head, Don gave me a wry smile, and we were off!

It seemed like the bosses had isolated us inside this boarded-up grave yard, so that with bits of disinfectant they could wipe out who and what we were.

On that first Saturday we trod between all those gravestones, some smashed and some not, laid out like huge dominoes with names and family histories carved out in order of death. There was a sadness I had never felt before. In a way it was even worse than Jennifer's still-born. There were still slabs of gravestones to be lifted and smashed but the bosses, whoever they were, thought it was better to start the process of lifting 'Whoever.' That's what they were often called: 'Whoever.' from the ground.

I was just two-foot down. Coffins? Where were the coffins? I kicked my spade through the clay, down again, and then cracked through into a family of bones. Bones of all sizes., but it hit me that there were so many tiny baby bones and doll-size skulls.

I found the first body, which was small enough to be a baby, in a watery jelly, the colour darker than black if that is possible. Before lifting it, Don gave me a slug of whisky to help wash away the taste. I lifted it from its parents, a baby still clinging to its relatives.  It was then that I realised I had to stop thinking.

74

Stop! Rick came across, offered me a Park Drive. We both took
hard drags on the cigs
We watched the other diggers lifting families and more
families. It seemed like the other diggers were just getting on
with it.

   "Don't think about it," said Rick. "Just think of you and Sandra
in Blackpool."
He left it at that and went back to working his patch.
I lifted more and more families and then carefully placed them
into a huge communal coffin. Then Carl started singing, 'Lily
the Pink.' Yes, there was laughter, the sort when you know it's
not the time or place for laughter but know it's inevitable or
you'd go mad.

We stood to the sides of the trenches where we had been
digging, there were bones and skulls lying all over the place.
Skulls, all sorts: babies', kids', men's and women's skulls; you
name it, of every size and shape.

We were all taking our time, making our excuses, as no one
wanted to go back in. We had been digging and exhuming
since about eight o'clock. There was a stench of coal, gas,
sulphur and diarrhoea all about the place, the worst I'd ever
experienced and, even worse, I seemed to be covered in it!

Bert thought we should take it slow as it was our first day and
have an early finish.
Half an hour to go before we finished that first shift and I was
just about getting into the rhythm of it. My mind had shifted to
Blackpool and the times me and Sandra had spent together.

## Hidden Depths – Peter Street

It was Rick who thanked God that this first dig was over, and everyone agreed and looked relieved. Our hands were covered, ingrained with unimaginable muck. I managed to clean my hands with a tiny rub of soap and a spoonful of sugar. Seeing my clean, sparkly hands, they teased me, saying it was due to too much masturbation!

\*\*\*

Saturday night and me and Sandra treated ourselves by going to see a film, 'The Family Way'. at the Capitol picture house. Later we walked back to the bus station eating pasties from Ye Old Pasty Shoppe and, in between mouthfuls, we talked money, houses and our wedding. It was Sandra who brought up exhuming. She admitted to scouring the newspapers for any evening jobs that would give extra money for our mortgage deposit. Her disappointment at not finding any work was clear to see. Over the weekend we talked more marriage plans and Sandra came up with the idea of having a very small wedding. Her brother's wedding cost £500 and her father promised he'd give us the same amount of money, which would certainly help.

\*\*\*

Astley Bridge cemetery. Monday morning. I was so surprised at how little we talked about the exhuming. There seemed to be a different atmosphere in the cabin. Quiet. Like something had been said out of place. Peculiarly, that week; there were no digs at Astley Bridge, Heaton or Tonge cemeteries. We started to put together some new staging which we'd long since needed. We were still not really speaking when Arnold, of all people, started singing 'Lily the Pink.' Rick and me joined in, singing as loudly as we could, followed by laughter, uncontrollable laughter. Sam came in to see what was happening. Seeing everything was OK, he returned to the cabin and fell back to sleep.

Monday night, Sandra finger-tipped the part-time job section in The Bolton Evening News: 'Earn £3.00 per night selling household goods on behalf of the disabled.' We were going for a quick interview with Harry, the boss of the household goods business. Harry asked us why we needed the extra money.

"Deposit for a mortgage," said Sandra seriously.

We were taken on and it was arranged we'd meet him the following night at six when he would drive us round to an estate where we would start our selling. So that was that, we were 'on the knock.' Sandra suggested I put my arm in a sling when we went out selling. We could be earning as much as £6 a night, if it worked out. It sounded too good to be true All great, until Sandra without any build up declared:

"Right, please can you pack in the Saturday work. It's not you." I'd never seen her look so determined. We compromised. I promised I would only work three more Saturdays. By that time most of the work would have been finished anyway And the next big exhuming job wouldn't be until the following year. Tuesday night. Harry, the boss took us to the newish Ladybridge estate, very posh. Approaching the first door we were as nervous as each other. As we knocked a dog started barking loudly. All that anticipation and then no-one answered until we knocked again, and a middle-aged woman opened the door.

"I am sorry to bother you," I said whilst patting my arm in the sling, "but I'm selling household goods on behalf of the disabled."

She rummaged through my bag looking at the stuff in there and bought two dish-cloths. Before Harry picked us up, two hours later, we had pitched to twenty or thirty houses. The £2.00 we made that night Sandra insisted was going towards a set of cooking pans. Two more nights and we had made a total of £7.00.

***

### *Second Exhuming Saturday*

The plan was to meet Sandra after work. She agreed I should carry my going-out clothes in my rucksack and then change into them at the end of my shift. Rick and Arnold had come early and were already squatting against the wooden hoardings of the site. The caravan was still stinking of toilet disinfectant. I changed from my ordinary clothes back into the boiler suit covered in the stench of dead bodies. They asked about Sandra. But they seemed to sense I was not myself.

"You're not on your own," said Arnold and Rick agreed. Five minutes later the others started walking onto the site. We were our body of eight again. First, we drank tea from heavily stained mugs. Then we made our way down the various trenches passing mounds of bones and bits of skulls. The stench of diarrhoea and sulphur seemed to hit us even harder than before. The paths we used to get to the main, long trench were maybe eight or nine-foot deep. As we walked down further, we found the sides had just fallen away. There were sets of skeletons piled on top of each other as if they had been thrown down in any old way. There were still no signs of coffins, no sign of anything except skeletons. No one had ever seen anything like it before.

We were in spook territory. There was a horrible feeling of separation from the scene before me. I felt like an alien, or even an abuser of sorts. Probably just me and my imagination!
At first, we carefully passed the bones up to the digger at ground level but as we dug deeper we became more carefree and, eventually, threw the bones up in any manner! It was like a ball game with skulls being thrown in all directions. The other diggers were laughing. There was more laughter and when I turned around to see what was happening. Rick pointed to a stack of skulls about ten feet behind me which had been thrown back down as a prank.
Later, Carl was astride a line of skulls when he picked one up. He shouted, "Catch!" throwing it like a rugby ball and then it went along the line towards the communal coffin.
 Laughter. Yes, we knew it was very wrong, but we just couldn't help it!
I was about six-foot down and the next spade-full had only a few bones with not much of anything else. The stench was minimal, or was I just getting used to it? Kicking in my spade, I hit solid. First, I stood astride it but then dared myself to put one foot on it. It had a soft up and down spring about it. I shouted for Rick. We had never seen a coffin solid like that before. Rick stayed up on top saying,

   "Keep on the rim, you don't want to go through that."
Now I was much more nervous.
I cleaned off the coffin as calmly and as best as I could. Rick finally came down and we started digging, tunnelling back

under the head and feet sections to give us more room to work. Don and Bert, wanting to know more, walked toward us through the mounds of clay, burnt clay pipes, bits of skulls, all mixed up with piles of nineteenth century death. They were walking, cracking on tiny bones and other human bits. The sounds and sights of it all was like a walk-through Hell!

"Can't remember," said Don, "last time I saw a lead coffin." Rick and me shrugged shoulders.

Nothing usually phased these men, these diggers, but that lead coffin did. That late Saturday morning there was a sullenness about them I hadn't seen before. Don didn't ask me to climb out, he ordered me out. It was the only time he ever raised his voice. They took a couple of minutes to get their thoughts together. We swapped places, and then he told us to get some ropes and a crowbar.

Don slotted the four-foot long crowbar in and prised the lid open. There was as 'shhhh..!' followed by a smell like nothing we'd smelt before, which completely painted the inside of our noses. The lid was fully back and there she was: fully clothed with her bonnet still in place. Her eyes had gone but there was a gossamer-like layer of skin, wrinkled, greasy, a bit like cold chicken skin after being oven cooked.

This was real horror film stuff. I didn't want to see her, but I couldn't take my eyes from that tiny woman. Don stood back, hit by the hundred-year or so death stench. Calmly, he lit up a smoke, pulled harder than hard. Flicked the fag, maybe six to eight feet away. And then he started the job of lifting her out as humanely as possible. Fine. Quiet, reverent like, until the lady he was lifting suddenly dropped one of her arms. It jerked me back and then after the shock of it, we again started laughing,

insane laughing, I was nearly hysterically as I shared that
particular sight and moment with Rick.

Fags out and burning, we all started singing: 'Lily the Pink.'
It took nearly an hour for us all to return to being sensible,
normal. Don went to place the woman in the huge communal
coffin as more bits fell from her. The giggles hit again, I think
mostly due to fright and being so disturbed by it. But there was
less laughter as we stood around wondering how to get the
lead coffin up and out when Bert shouted down:

"Try folding it up."

It was becoming more fantastical by the second. Rick and me
looked at each other, nodded, then with all the others started
the job of trying to get the coffin out of its burial place, with the
ropes. I don't think I could ever compare anything to those few
minutes. What on this earth could be compared to lifting an
empty lead coffin? Once on top, we wondered how to deal
with it. Lead is a soft metal. Soft enough to fold or bend over, if
you hit it hard enough. The gang of us hammered it until, it did
fold-up... though quite how I still don't know? Once folded,
Bert called lunch time.

We took off our stinking overalls and with very little soap and
water available went about trying to clean ourselves up as best
as we could, then went to 'Ye Olde Pasty Shoppe.' I wasn't so
sure about eating anything after what we had seen and done,
but I did! Incredibly, I even managed two pasties. The other
diggers sat around eating lunch and smoking; then we had a
bottle or two of beer.

Everyone relaxed, as though they were on a family picnic. It
was then, more than any other time, I realised the men I was

with, were a special breed. These seven men who had taken me on with no questions asked, treated me no different from anyone else. Together we had seen, and had come through something, most people would never, ever want to experience. It was like working in a war zone or (God forbid) a death camp. Later in the afternoon there were more lead coffins and more bits falling from those semi-preserved bodies. What I didn't get was why none had eyes whilst other body parts were still intact. All in all, it had been an extraordinary Saturday of spooks, songs, jokes, fags and pasties.

\*\*\*

Before meeting Sandra later, I enjoyed time in the Bridge Street Slipper Baths. Snorting bubbles up my nose trying to rid it of dead bodies, but unfortunately this only stung the inside and did nothing for the stench. Everywhere that awful smell went with me. Even Sandra's expensive perfume from Woolworth's didn't get rid of it.
Sunday, we went to Mass at St. William's, the Catholic church we were going to get married in, and later we walked around Bolton town centre. Again, checking out the various estate agent's windows. We worked two nights on the knock that week and earned £12.

\*\*\*

### Third Exhuming Saturday
The caravan was bursting with all the reeking overalls and death-covered clogs. We rested outside, rather than inside the caravan, which had become for emergency toilet use only. We were now working down in a maze of trenches.

I have no sense of direction whatsoever and got panicky, not knowing my left from my right. In the third trench to my left was a body but there was supposed to be one on the right.

"No, we mean our left not your left, our left."

In the end I just rested and enjoyed a Park Drive. Fine, until a bucket of tiny bones was poured down on me. I couldn't help being childish by throwing some of them back up at the laughing men above.

"Dinner time," Bert shouted.

In the Market Hall, eight exhumers were all stinking of diarrhoea, coal gas, and, worst of all, dead bodies, mingled with weak disinfectant. Once again, our clogs sparked over the Market Hall floor. People around us were pulling faces. Some walked away, but Bert and the other diggers just walked past towards the bacon stall:

"Eight bacon butties," Don asked for. He turned around:

"Brown sauce?" We all nodded.

The smell and the thoughts of it all began to hit me. I felt I wanted to vomit but didn't. It was like they knew and when Don handed me a bacon butty he told me to:

"Get it down your neck! Make you feel better."

I didn't (still don't) know why I started laughing? Maybe it was the way they just tucked into their food with melted butter dripping down those filthy fingers which ten minutes before had been handling dead bodies. We walked back, ready to cross the road and cars suddenly stopped to let us pass.

OK it was just coincidence, but I really couldn't help thinking it was the drivers seeing us as special,

We pushed our way through the wooden doors into the site to the half empty trenches, like a Somme or a Flanders from all those years ago. We went through, what I called, 'journey

83

trenches' with their burnt-out clay pipes now fossilised in dark soil. In his trench, Carl found an 1860 penny piece which he later handed in to the Museum.

***

*Last Exhuming Saturday.*

After the dig I was going to meet my future mother in-law who was pressurising me to give up grave-digging. She had always insisted I hadn't under any circumstance to tell anyone what job I did. Exhuming was definitely a strictly no-go area. I was going to meet her for a coffee in a nice town centre coffee house. My future in-laws never accepted my epilepsy and my father-in-law said:

"If you were OK, like us (I think he meant normal) I'd get you down on the pit face with me."

I couldn't say I'd rather do grave-digging and exhuming because going down a mine on the pit face was the last place on earth I wanted to work.

When I mentioned to Rick about it being my last Saturday, he wasn't at all bothered. The opposite even:

"My brother is longing for a bit of work." he said.

That was it. me and the rest of the team were happy. Saying that, I still shouldn't have mentioned about it being my last Saturday. Even more I shouldn't have mentioned meeting my mother in-law and what she thought about me and grave-digging, and as for exhuming...

Anyway, it was going to be the same plan as with Sandra, extra clothes, slipper baths. Smart, in my best walking out clothes. No, it was more than silly telling it all to the team

84

Behind the hoarding, kicking the spade into the section furthest from the back lane, I hit wet. The feel of it was so different. Don seemed to know and asked if I wanted to swap places, but I said "no." I was about a foot down and had started cutting out nine-inch blocks of clay when Don brought me a bucket to dip my spade in, to help the clay slide off. With that he was back to his own business. Fine, everything was going great. Later in the morning Don came over to me and handed me a bottle of whiskey. I took a tot, glug and the warm feeling all over, I gave the bottle to Rick, then round it passed one to another until it was returned back to Don.

I was back kicking in the spade and lifting wet heavy cubes up and slamming them on top of the pile of clay. About a couple of feet down I hit wood. But it wasn't too solid and seemed to split easily. However, there seemed to be something different about it, heavy and kind of squishy. I smashed through an almost intact coffin. I began to lift bodies with skin hanging off like bits of cloth. My hands were splodging about in a colloid jelly and I was half way through lifting out half skinned bodies when Bert shouted:

"Lunch Time".

All agreed to go for a pub lunch in The Boar's Head, a well-known place for 'Irish on the Spade.' I'd never had a pub lunch before. So aye, I was up for that. We cleaned up as best we could in the circumstances.

The Boar's Head was crowded with what looked and sounded like Irish manual workers. Bert bought me a meat & potato pie. Don bought me the first pint of best beer. Rick supplied the fags. They said it was a celebration for them all, but Rick quietly said it was more for me, especially for my last day after my very first exhumation.

I was half way through my second pint when the team started singing, 'Lily the Pink.' Everyone in the pub joined in. Every time someone else came in the pub, regardless of who they were, 'Lily the Pink' was sung even louder.

I don't know why I shouted out that my mother was Irish from a Republican family and my grandfather had been involved in the uprising of 1916. But that brought about even more singing, especially from the Irish in the bar. Fourth pint, so I am told, and I was wobbling. After my fifth pint the team carried me out and back to the site where they laid me down in one of the empty coffins. When I awoke about an hour or so later my overalls were off, but my stinking clogs were still firmly laced onto my feet.

I was later told that Rick helped me half way down to where I was meeting my future Mother-in-law. He even managed to get me there on time and then left. Sandra told me I was still stinking of dead bodies mixed with bits of vomit. Though my jeans were almost clean. I really don't remember placing my dirty hands on my Mother-in-law's clean coat, a new coat or so I was told. A coat which was never seen again.

My exhuming career was over!

\*\*\*

## Chapter 9

## Home our Home

*Autumn 1969.*

My exhuming days were over and at least my in-laws were pleased. My boss understood the reasons.

"One of those things," was all he said, then he folded his arms, pulled his moth sideways and said:

"You can have Frank's job while he's on sick leave, he's got a note for six weeks."

Frank was the weekend cemetery keeper. There was a long pause before he said,

"I'll give you time and a half."

He changed, sterner:

"No excuses. If you mess up you can say goodbye to anything else like this."

I promised.

"You can start this Saturday."

Speechless is not me, but I was that day. Of course, I accepted. Sandra was so pleased as it not only meant more money, easy money but we could also give up selling on the knock too.

Me and Sandra spent the weekend walking around the Tonge cemetery. I took her down to the Nuns' section. She told me how the nuns at her school would slap the children's legs hard with a wooden, twelve-inch ruler if they stepped out of line.

***

Late September. The Graham Ball estate agent on Bradshawgate was advertising a house we thought was perfect. Yes, they gave

87

us the keys and let us look around on our own. But the selling price of £2,000 was too much for us. Before we left the estate agent's Sandra asked if there were any more houses more around the eighteen or nineteen hundred mark?

"We have a stone cottage in Barrow Bridge."

Barrow Bridge was one of my childhood playgrounds with its boating lake at the top of the lane where the man in a yellow jumper used to shout: 'Come in number three…!' There was an ice cream shop, fields, farms and the famous sixty-three steps which Mum used to help me climb when I was a child. It was the place where all the mill and pit workers used to visit on Good Friday.

The key, our key, was for a house on Second Street, Barrow Bridge. I took in a deep breath, held out my hand to the Estate Agent, like I was receiving the Eucharist. Half an hour later, me and Sandra became time travellers with thirty-five steps walking us back to 1820 where old fashioned, end-of-street gas lamps lit up each row of cottages. There were no cars, only elderly people tending their gardens. Sandra commented on there being a 'louder than loud' cemetery silence.

We approached the house on Second Street. We held hands but couldn't speak, we were too excited.

"Let me do it," she said.

I passed the key over to her. She looked at me as she pushed the door into a corridor, we looked at each other. We knew then, this was for us. This was going to be our house, our home! There was a small front room to our left and a smell of old books and elderly people. The kitchen was big with no fire place. No radiators. Nothing, well, except for a working electric cooker hiding inside a large wooden box. The sink, fridge and a washing machine had been built into their own tiny room under the stairs. Sandra thought it was cute. I thought it was stupid, but I could see the practical side of it.

We checked out the back street. 'Somewhere safe' is what she wanted… this was ideal.

Once outside, we walked back down the wide steps back to 1969 where a Number 4 bus was getting ready to leave. It looked like we were going to miss it, but it stopped, and the bus conductor, at the back of the bus, swung round the steel pole, shouting (in Italian) 'Ciao!' Then something else in Italian, then in English:

"You two young people are wanting this bus?"

\*\*\*

Dad didn't mean to wipe out our excitement, but again began reminding me about socialism and betraying the working classes. He did not see it as a kind of progression, he thought it was something evil. I think deep down he was worried about me becoming a 'Tory.' He even talked about an appointment with his old landlord.

"You have to rent," Dad shouted.

He started talking about my epilepsy, what would happen if it worsened? He finally calmed down and said he would sort everything. We just needed to see Mr Grundy who would get us a house.

I didn't respond.

Me and Sandra wanted to sort ourselves out. Do it our way!

He didn't understand. I think it was an age thing as he was born in the Victorian times of 1895, when it was so different. Regardless, me and Sandra were already on the starting line of home ownership. We had paid the £250 deposit, plus £75 legal fees. About six weeks later the house on Second Street, Barrow Bridge, was ours.

House achieved, we planned our wedding for December 20th at St. William's Catholic Church. We talked about guests and Sandra was absolutely determined and definite:

"No gaffs and no gravediggers." Compromises were made, and we agreed that I could have gravediggers at my Stag night, on the condition I didn't drink a drop of booze, I gave my word.

\*\*\*

December. One week to our wedding when a dig came in, a four-foot-six. The boss told us it was for a guy known as Pedro, or something like, who was from Jamaica. We thought it was a joke. For a start when the boss gave me the burial chit, it simple read: 'Male: 30 years old, Catholic, row eighty, four-foot-six deep.'

That was all. Just deep enough for one coffin. Only four-foot-six, no relatives. He, whoever he was, was going to be alone. Not only that, there were two men wearing long dirty cream coloured raincoats and fedoras down near the main gates. There were a couple more down near the back gate on the other side of the cemetery. There were four men dressed like Philip Marlowe private detectives (Humphrey Bogart and Robert Mitchum) smoking cigarettes stylishly while setting up cameras on tripods at various angles. Every so often one of them would step out from the dark of the heavy lines of rhododendrons, take a few peeks around, then vanish back from where he had come from.

By now I had cut out the shape of the grave, all ready to start digging, when more Philip Marlowes climbed over the wall and hid behind the rhododendrons. I needed to know what was happening. Yes, there was a good chance that I would mess up but if there were any problems I would look to Rick and Arnold. If the strangers wanted to start something, Arnold and Rick would be more than happy to oblige them.

Nodding at me, Rick lit up a cigarette, rolled up his sleeves, and then walked with Arnold, over towards where the men were still setting up more cameras on more tripods. Within minutes my friends had also disappeared into the dark of the rhododendrons. There was no shouting, no movement, just a whisper of voices. Minutes later Arnold came out, followed by Rick. Arnold pointed at the grave: 'Hit and Run.' He handed out the cigarettes. Rick did his Zippo thing, then it was Arnold who started off with:

"That's Pedro from the fire?"

Rick pulled hard on his fag.

"That's what you call bad."

Arnold was nodding, while I'd not a clue what they were talking about, though I sure wanted to know more.

"That club was doing so well."

"There was talk about gangs who wanted to take over, but he was having none of that. So, they forced him out."

"That's what I heard," answered Rick.

"It was arson all right. Sure as eggs are eggs."

They looked back towards the men in the bushes and told me to get on with the 'Hit and Run.' This was the first time I had been involved in a mystery, but who could tell me more? Maybe the funeral director... he must know, he'd been doing it since the year dot? I'd ask him when I got a chance.

I asked Arnold if it was murder and how many died?

"Can't remember," answered Arnold. "It was well over a dozen."

I was agog

"So, it's all pointing to murder?"

Arnold shrugged his shoulders.


Then he left me to the dig. Four-foot-six, no problem. Easy, especially after that last grave, a nine-footer when the sides collapsed just after I climbed out. That would have been the end of me! I made that four-foot-sixer even easier by building the wooden staging on a forty-degree slant. So, by tunnelling under the stack all the soil and clay, would slide back more or less of its own accord. I even carried two slates ready for the top of the coffin, so the weight of the falling earth wouldn't crash through onto this 'Pedro.' Just above waist height and I had slotted in two seven-foot wooden sides. OK, the wooden head blocks had been difficult but after I pissed on them they slid in nicely. Simple. My curiosity made me climb out and carried me over to the two nearest coppers. They would only tell me what Arnold had already found out: 'Hit and Run from the A6.' Apart from the priest, funeral director and me, there was no one else there. The coppers trying their best to be invisible with cameras on tripods didn't count.

## Hidden Depths – Peter Street

Arnold kept an eye on me, the coppers and anything else that was moving. Father Barr, was looking over at me curiously. Again, I shrugged my shoulders. All I knew was that I was burying a 'Hit and Run victim called Pedro from Jamaica.' Father Barr gave me a puzzled look, as though I should have made it my business to find out who I was burying. Confused I went back to the grave. I was just placing a couple of handfuls of sand and soil into the box when I looked up to see the hearse creeping through the double cast iron gates, like one giant black beetle. No mourners. No follow-on cars. No back-up. No family, just one slow, five-mile-an-hour hearse. Only the various Philip Marlowe's about the place, but it was like we were burying a pauper. A very young pauper called Pedro. But even for a pauper there are usually some old dears about the cemetery, visiting the grave of a relative or friend, who would then stand around watching the funeral, to see if they could recognise anyone. Someone there to bow their heads. This day, this funeral, there was no-one. The whole cemetery was completely empty and there was a deafening silence.

We were carrying his coffin over to the grave when I was asked to be a mourner. I couldn't refuse. We threaded the rope through the brass rings and lowered him down into his forever. I even recited (under my breath) some of the service with Father Barr and said a 'Hail Mary' for him and then threw in a handful of dirt from the box onto his coffin.
Afterwards, the undertaker and me swapped all the usual niceties about my family. He even asked if all our wedding plans were going OK. As I was thanking him, he, surprisingly, gave me the usual five-bob tip. He had a reputation for

knowing everything that had happened in the town, sometimes before it had actually happened, so I couldn't resist asking him about Pedro.

"He was seen running away, from the fire, so everyone assumed he had something to do with it."

"What fire? Why run away if he had nothing to do with it?" I asked.

Excited, like he was part of some great mystery he told me more. I wasn't sure if I believed him or not when he talked about arson with over a dozen dead. Some of them had jumped out of the only window which was not blocked up and sadly thudded onto the iron railings or fallen into the almost dry river bed a long way below. It was then he screwed up his face.

"It's funny you know," he said. "The only window it was safe to jump from, couldn't be opened. Funny that don't you think?" I waited whilst he gathered his thoughts. He went on to tell me that someone thought a professional job had been done on the window. He wouldn't reveal who told him.

"My worst job ever was lifting those young bodies off those spiked railings."

Yes, I was getting more interested by the minute. But was it real? Or was it just another of his stories that he'd teased me with over the years? He looked back at the two coppers who seemed to know what was being said.

I later found out even they, the coppers, didn't know about those six bodies which had been stacked in one of the cleaning rooms at the Town Hall as the morgue had been full up. Anyway, he said, that was the rumour! The worst part was the trauma suffered by the cleaning lady the following day when she went to get her cleaning materials from that room and saw

94

the bodies. The shock, so we were told, nearly killed her. We also heard that because the burnt flesh of those dead young people smelt so much like roasted pig she never ate bacon again. There was a shrug of shoulders. I thought someone should have told her, or at the very least left her a message, something like: 'No entry: Dead bodies.' I know we shouldn't have but we laughed at that.

As for the cleaning lady, she never worked again.

By now the whole story was getting complicated, out of hand and I was loving it. It was truly one of his best stories ever. He took out a fag packet and offered me a Senior Service, then turned and offered the same to the Philip Marlowe's. They refused. My head was thumping with all sorts of questions. He lit up, sucked deeply on his fag then blew smoke out. 'Open Verdict.' He looked doubtful even with all his years of experience this seemed incredible to him, he said,

"Open Verdict my bum!"

I knew there was more to this story and I asked about Pedro. Another Senior Service, this time he was more relaxed and blew out smoke rings.

"He panicked after hearing those bodies thudding in the river and on the railings and he ran. Wouldn't you if you heard that?"

He was ready to move off when he suddenly looked sideways at me and said:

"Pedro wasn't his real name, you know, and he didn't even come from Jamaica."

After gathering my thoughts together, I tried asking more questions, but he turned and hurried off to his car and sped off.

The coppers looked at each other then back at me. Yes, I wanted to know even more, all the who, what, where and when? But they dodged my questions. They showed no emotion, so I sort of guessed what they were going to say next because I was thinking the same.

"Well they got him in the end."
It was getting more detective TV programme by the minute. Then, they came out with it again. "They got him in the end." I didn't understand why they were giggling.

\*\*\*

Sunday. Six days to go to our wedding and it was me who wanted to start some work in 'Our House', especially that section under the stairs. Sandra having more important things to think about, gave way to me knocking down that section, a smallish job using hammers and a couple of bags for the rubbish. Easy-peasy! I unscrewed the door and hammered down the wooden partition separating kitchen and the bit under the stairs, which was going to give us more space.

Sandra again asked if everything was going to be cleaned up for our first night in our new home. I promised. Every night I'd work until late to get everything perfect.
Monday evening, everything had gone well. Until, Sandra came to see how it was going and we discovered that the partitions I had started to smash down were stuffed with some fifty-year-old newspapers, horse hair and old rags. Sandra was worried.

"No problem." I replied then started to rip everything out. It had to be done. About twenty minutes later we started scratching. There were tiny insects trampolining all over Sandra and she saw the same thing was happening to me. Not only that, but there was also, what I can only describe as a black mist, in front of us.

"Fleas," shouted Sandra. "Bathroom quick."
I was about to rip off my clothes when Sandra warned me against it. Calm. She ran the bath, she ordered me to get in the bath fully clothed. We both climbed in and let the water drown the hundreds of fleas covering all of our bodies and our clothes. By now Sandra was furious:

"The last thing we needed was the house..."
She interrupted herself. Yes, she was on the verge of crying. It was the first time she had ever raised her voice:

"What are we going to be coming home to?"
I promised it would all be cleared up. But Sandra wasn't convinced, and she phoned her dad to come and collect us. We climbed in to his car with just towels covering our embarrassment.

Tuesday: Sandra phoned the pest control people to sort the fleas out. Rick and me were opening a six-footer but I couldn't concentrate. In the end I confessed to making a complete 'balls up' at home. Rick kept saying:

"Don't worry, everything will turn out OK."
It was all right for him, he wasn't getting married in a couple of days' time!

Wednesday evening: By then, I was very tired with having to sweep up and carry bits of old plaster and wood out into the front garden. But the great thing was the Pest Control man had come and done a great job of killing all the pests.

Thursday: I managed to talk with all the diggers about my Stag night. None would say where my non-alcoholic night was going to be held. I kept that part quiet from Sandra, who between tears, again insisted, "no Gaffs". I promised.

Rick came to our house and helped with the cleaning up. We stayed until nearly midnight and I paid for his taxi home.

Friday: I took the day off and worked on the house all morning, until finally it was all spick and span.

Friday evening: Stag night. I was to meet the other seven diggers along with my future brother-in-law outside the very respectable Swan Hotel. Sandra would have been impressed. That was until Joe suggested we go instead, to the not so salubrious, Fleece Hotel, across the road. There the huge, tough-looking doormen nodded to the other diggers. They stopped me. It was Don who said it was my Stag night and I was with them. They smiled, moved to one side and let me in.

Downstairs was absolutely 'chock-a-block.' Upstairs was even worse, but the women there seemed different to the ones downstairs. They wore bright red feathers fluffing above purple or orange hats that were cocked to one side and clipped in place, tight over dyed hair. Some of those wearing brightly coloured hats were sitting facing the main bar, where most of the men were drinking hard.

It was half an hour later, Cornelius came in with his brother Michael. Phil Maurice was already there too as was Fowkes. I hadn't invited them, but they were there, just a few of the Gaffs, great! There were more nods between one or two of the diggers and the Gaffs, who only stayed for a few minutes then left. I felt a little uneasy that they had left. It was as if I had somehow let them down.  But, I stayed sober.

### Saturday 20th December: Wedding Day.

Everything went as a wedding is supposed to go, that was until I had to sign the marriage certificate. On no account, according to my now mother-in-law, had I to write 'gravedigger' as my occupation.

There were just thirteen of us at our wedding. That was OK, as Sandra and me were spending the rest of the wedding money on new carpets and a three-piece suite.  Sandra didn't want me to carry her over the threshold into our perfectly spotless free-of-all-fleas house. Perfect.

\*\*\*

Two weeks later I was back at Heaton cemetery. Bob, the foreman, gave me a six-footer which had just come in. Don helped me build the staging. He said he'd come back when he thought I would be needing someone to throwback.  I felt a tingling and strange feeling running up and down my legs. My mind felt like it was going backwards. I must have been at least five-foot down in the dig because I just about remember Don coming back. I remember his shovel, flat, on the boarding waiting for my next spit of the grave. I remember shoving my spade a spit down, testing for depth. I even remember clonking the slates on top of the next coffin. But after that is blank.

I woke in hospital. My mouth was hurting. Mud was all over the bed sheets. I couldn't move my shoulder it was hurting badly, and I somehow knew I'd dislocated it. Don was sitting at the bedside.

"You feel funny. Jesus! I had a job lifting you up. You're heavier than you look!"

"You lifted me out?" I managed to say.

"Bert and me!"

"We were going to leave you and go to the next grave, but your shoulder gave way again and it was an ambulance job." I tested my shoulder, but it still wouldn't move My mouth felt like I'd been chewing a mixture of red hot coals and razor blades. The x-ray confirmed my shoulder was dislocated.

They kept me in hospital longer than usual until an orthopaedic surgeon was free. It was something to do with my shoulder which kept dislocating. I had to go back and see them in three weeks' time. Meanwhile I had to keep my arm in a sling. No grave-digging. No work!  When I walked into the cabin about six weeks later there was a cheer and best wishes. On my return, I was given a four-foot-sixer. Easy. But, about two- foot down my shoulder started hurting and it dislocated again.

I knew then my digging days were over.

\*\*\*

## *EPILOGUE*

At the end, I was leaving a world most people wouldn't want to go in to for a variety of reasons, be it nightmares or the degrading physical aspects. For some, a grave-digger is a person who is on the outside of society. A freak even. Maybe for some, but certainly not for me. I was now near that old cabin with its cast iron range, its domino table, its stone flagged floor and I am now heading towards those cast-iron gates. All those memories and mad times suddenly just slotted up on either side of that narrow strip of tarmac road, huge like on cinema screens, all showing the best of those four years.

From being lifted out of a sand hell-hole to catching skulls, to hammering lead coffins into a shape so we could more easily fold them up. Seeing myself being laid out in that coffin after they had got me 'pissed & pissed again.' It was all there. With those men who in their own way were completely 'barking,' every one of them, from one giant man who wanted to be invisible and definitely not heard, to Rick, the Brian Jones lookalike, not forgetting Arnold the ex-bare-knuckle fighter, yes, barking of course, but my dear Lord, each one of them had held my hand and walked me through the trials that came my way. They had been there, listened, teased and even saved my life. Wonderful!

Finally, stepping out through those cast iron gates I was back regrettably on the map, back in society, where I sobbed and sobbed, while at the same time realising they had been preparing me for anything ... anything life could throw at me. For better or for worse I was now Me!

## GLOSSARY

1. **Gaffs or Gaff Lads** was originally the name for the fairground hands who built and ran the rides though later it became a general name for all fairground workers. It is derived from '*Gaffer*'

2. **Grave sizes:** Four-foot-six refers to the depth of the grave and this is the minimum depth which allows for one-foot-six-inches for the coffin with three-foot of earth on top. Other types of grave are dug to depths of: six-foot, seven-foot-six-inches, nine-foot, ten-foot-six-inches and even, on rare occasions, twelve-foot. The grave is generally seven-foot four-inches long and three-foot wide at the top tapering to about half that at the bottom.

3. **A Grand Mal seizure** is caused by abnormal electrical activity throughout the brain and results in a loss of consciousness and violent muscle contractions. It's very common in Epileptics like Peter and can be very serious, in some cases causing death.

4. **The Log Book** was a legal requirement for a lorry driver to have and record details of their journeys in. This was often checked at the road-side by the police. By holding up a log book, other lorry drivers would be more likely to stop and pick up a fellow driver.

5. **A Vault** is a container made of brick (concrete today) that encloses a coffin to help prevent a grave from sinking. Wooden coffins (or caskets) decompose, and often the weight of earth on top of the coffin, or the passage of heavy cemetery maintenance equipment

over it, can cause the casket to collapse and the soil above it to settle, the vault helps to prevent this.

6. **Bessemer** is used here to indicate the waste product produced by the Bessemer process which converts iron to steel. The process removed impurities from the iron by heating it and skimming off the impurities which were lighter than the steel. The slag the process produce was of no use and was dumped.

7. **The Welsh Tabernacle** didn't have a graveyard. The graveyard Peter and Co exhumed belonged to an earlier chapel on the same site. This was the Oliver Chapel which was so successful it outgrew the Ridgeway Gates site and moved to St Georges Road in 1863 where it is now the St Andrew & St George Church. The Welsh Tabernacle people took on the disused Ridgeway Gates chapel in 1906 but mustn't have been allowed to bury anyone in the old graveyard. No wonder few coffins survived except for the lead ones as the graves were well over 100 years old.

8. **Top Storey Club fire** is the one referred to in Chapter nine in which 19 people died at a Bolton club. Go to this link to find out more about it: https://tinyurl.com/yagd2rd6. Later in life, when he was working for the BBC, Peter gained access to official and unofficial records of the fire and talked to policemen who were involved in the investigation. This may well result in a future publication.